THE

FUTURE BRITISH
SURFACE FLEET

THE
FUTURE BRITISH
SURFACE FLEET

OPTIONS FOR MEDIUM-SIZED NAVIES

D K BROWN

CONWAY

MARITIME PRESS

© D K Brown 1991

First published in Great Britain 1991 by
Conway Maritime Press
101 Fleet Street
London EC4Y 1DE

British Library Cataloguing in Publication Data
Brown, D. K. (David Keith) 1928 –
The future British surface fleet: options
for medium sized navies.
1. Great Britain. Navies
I. Title
359.00941

ISBN 0-85177-557-8

Typeset by Swanston Graphics, Derby
Printed and bound by The Bath Press, Bath

Contents

Foreword

Strategy should govern the type of ships to be designed. Ship design, as dictated by strategy, should govern tactics. Tactics should govern the details of armament.

ADMIRAL J FISHER, 1904

The close interaction between design, tactics and strategy noted by Admiral Fisher seems to justify this venture by a Naval Constructor into a general discussion of naval warfare. The views put forward here on future war at sea are not revolutionary but differ in some aspects from today's accepted views and, together with a consideration of resources, lead to a different fleet mix.

These views are personal views. Long experience shows that strong personal views are always incomplete and often wrong but, even if wrong, may provoke fruitful discussion. Such discussion is valuable because warship design is a team effort – or should be.

The irregular verb 'to design'

I create
You interfere
He gets in the way

We co-operate
You obstruct
They conspire

DKB, 1983

This book is based on a paper which I wrote for my old department to mark my retirement in 1988. At that time the Warsaw Pact was strong and seemingly united, presenting a major threat to NATO on both land and sea. Since then the Pact has collapsed but the

Soviet navy is as powerful as it ever was; old ships may have been discarded in considerable numbers but the rate at which powerful new ships are entering service has not diminished. Who can be sure that the present Soviet leadership will survive as their economic policy leads to hardship in the short term and greater freedom permits militant nationalism to grow? The possibility exists either of the emergence of an aggressive nationalist leadership or of a counter-coup by hardline communists; in either case a new, aggressive leadership might yet decide to use the capability of the navy to stop the seaborne trade on which Europe depends.

Britain has been close to defeat at sea twice this century as a result of submarine blockade. Though this country is slightly less vulnerable today, Western Europe as a whole is at much greater risk due to its dependency on imported oil. Britain and Western Europe depend on the sea and can be defeated there; only the Soviet Navy has the capability to inflict such a defeat. This justifies its role as the principal threat in much of this book.

While the draft of this book was being revised, news came of Iraq's invasion of Kuwait, and of the response from the United States and the United Kingdom. I was pleased that the draft needed no great change, as militant governments in the Middle East had already been recognised as the secondary threat. Operations outside the range of home based fighter aircraft expose the Royal Navy's weakness in air defence with, at best, a few Harriers and an ageing medium range missile, Sea Dart.

Alternative approaches are suggested to age-old and insoluble problems such as quality versus quantity, the size of ships, and the realisation of qualities such as seaworthiness, battleworthiness and endurance. The interaction between the customer (the Royal Navy), the paymaster (the Government), and industry is re-examined in the light of both British and American experience. To few if any of these problems is there a right answer, only different shades of opinion.

I had hoped to avoid the use of initials, acronyms etc but I have found this impossible. It would have needed a much longer book to spell out anti-submarine warfare or mine countermeasures vessel each time. However, such abbreviations are few, are explained when first used, and are listed in a glossary. SWATH is frequently mentioned: for those unfamiliar with this type of vessel, a picture of an early study is included and there is a description in Appendix 1.

PATROL   VESSEL   (MID 90'S)

An early study for a SWATH OPV. The excellent seakeeping of the SWATH is of value in many roles.

Through the views are my own, I must acknowledge the value of discussions with many of my colleagues and others, particularly Norman Friedman. I must also thank the Royal Institution of Naval Architects for permission to reproduce material from my papers and, at the same time, apologise that so many references are to my own work - after all, this is a personal view.

Thanks are also due for permission to use illustrations to: Carrington Shipyards, the Science Museum, Vosper Thornycroft, YARD, and Yarrow Shipbuilders.

I must emphasise, finally, that the views expressed here are mine and not necessarily those of the Ministry of Defence or any other organisation.

Postscript, added after the liberation of Kuwait

'Instant' lessons from a war are rarely valid, but the temptation to suggest a few is irresistible. Clearly, I had failed to appreciate that world peace counts as a vital interest of the United Kingdom and that support of such military actions as that in the Gulf is a primary, not a secondary, role for the Navy.

On the tactical level one may note the value of Tomahawk strikes from an unexpected direction and the overwhelming success of the helicopter-launched Sea Skua missile (see page 35) against fast attack craft.

The importance of mine warfare was shown by the damage to USS *Tripoli* and USS *Princeton*, the only Allied ships damaged in the war. Since the ceasefire I have been to the Gulf to study the mine clearance operation and am filled with admiration for the Hunt class and their highly skilled crews.

DKB
April 1991

1

Introduction: The Political and Strategic Background

In the very simplest terms, sea power gives the ability to use the sea for one's own purposes, such as the transport of supplies or the movement of armies, while denying such use to the enemy. Pressure can be exerted by economic blockade, by reinforcement of armies, by invasion or by striking directly at targets in the enemy country.

Until the mid nineteenth century transport by water was much easier and quicker than transport by land, which a gave a sea power such as England the advantage in fighting a land power such as France. In particular, Wellington's Peninsular War depended on sea power for victory, as the Duke himself observed. By the second half of the nineteenth century, the network of railways had shifted the transport equation in favour of the central land mass, first recognised by Sir Halford J Mackinder.[1] One may see the failure of the peripheral campaigns of World War I, such as the Dardenelles and Salonika, as the triumph of railways over the steamship. The loss of sea power's ability to defeat a land power has obscured the vital truth that nations which live by the sea are uniquely vulnerable to catastrophe through defeat at sea.

Most people who play games are familiar with the so called 'zero-sum game', in which players of equal skill have the same chance of winning, the stakes are equal and one player's gain is the other's loss. The theoretical study of war has much in common with the

---

[1] The most convenient source for the writings of Mackinder, a famous geographer of about 1904, is:
Paul M Kennedy, *The Rise and Fall of British Naval Mastery* (London, 1976). This book includes full references to the original sources.

mathematical theory of games, but also covers situations in which gains and losses are not equal, in which one player cannot win and must play for a draw as the only alternative to losing. War at sea may fall into this category; NATO could not defeat the Warsaw Pact (or any other great land power) by winning a new Battle of the Atlantic – but it could be defeated there.

The threat at sea to NATO, and particularly to its Western European members, can be considered under two main scenarios. The best known postulates interruption of the reinforcement convoys to NATO's land fronts, where reinforcements are possibly even more important as the US Army in Europe is reduced.

It is estimated that 800 ship lifts would be needed in the first 30 days of war to bring US forces and their equipment across the Atlantic. A single armoured division needs 100,000 tonnes of cargo space, of which some 40 percent consists of items too large to fit into a standard container. Such a division needs a further 1000 tonnes of supplies, mainly petrol and oil, to keep it fighting (see Appendix 2). The task of moving British reinforcements across the North Sea must also be considered; this is a simple task if unopposed, but such reinforcements are very vulnerable to attack in the event of hostilities. Reinforcements to Northern Norway are also very vulnerable to attack.[2]

The second scenario, economic blockade, has not been given much attention in recent years. It is certain that the United Kingdom was close to defeat by starvation during the U-boat campaign in 1917. Sinkings of merchant ships at about ten per day were far in excess of new construction until the convoy system was introduced. Churchill wrote of World War II that 'the only thing that ever really frightened me during the war was the U Boat peril...'.[3] Closer study suggests that the peril was less than in the earlier war, mainly due to the massive US building programme of both merchant ships and escorts.

---

[2] Some well-known fictional accounts of World War III and the struggle to get reinforcements across the Atlantic are well worth study, for example:

Tom Clancy, *Red Storm Rising* (New York, 1986)

Sir John Hackett, *The Third World War* (London, 1978)

John Wingate, *Carrier* (London, 1981)

Even if you reject their approach, these novels should provoke thought.

[3] Winston S Churchill, *The Second World War, Vol II* (London, 1948).

The decline in the strength of the British Merchant Navy is most worrying; only one of the fifteen ships chartered to take 7th Armoured Brigade to Kuwait was British. In an emergency, British ships can be requisitioned, but others must be chartered, if their owners are willing and insurers can be found. The loyalty and dedication of British merchant crews has been amply demonstrated, but through crews of other nations have fought bravely alongside British crews, it cannot be assumed that this will always be so. The catastrophic fall in recruitment of British officers and crew is perhaps more worrying than the decline in numbers of ships.

Solutions are not easy; international agreements seek to prevent the use of subsidies, and yet substandard ships and inadequately trained crews are still too common. Much military planning involves the use of Ro-Ro ships, and even those with passenger certificates fall well short of the standards now seen necessary even for peacetime operation.

Western Europe is far more dependent on seaborne supplies, mainly of oil, than was the case in the past. In peacetime, annual imports of oil are between 400 and 500 million tonnes (see Appendix 3) and even minor interruptions as a result of Middle East wars have shown how great can be the disruption caused. Germany, Italy and France are most vulnerable. Some 90 million tonnes of oil imports to Europe come by pipeline from the USSR (and these would stop at once in the event of war with that country); nearly 200 million tonnes come from the vulnerable North Sea installation, and the rest by sea. Western Europe can now feed itself, but even this ability rests on the annual import, by sea, of 20,000 tonnes of phosphate fertiliser and on the inbuilt overproduction of the much-maligned 'Common Agricultural Policy'.

The USA is far less dependent on seaborne trade. Through 30 percent of her oil is imported, there is great scope for reducing consumption, which has fallen less than in other developed countries in recent years, and in using alternative supplies at slightly higher cost. The USA exports about 4 percent of its Gross National Product, compared with 3 percent for the Soviet Union, another central landmass, 25 percent for the UK and 14 percent for Japan.

It is not hard to visualise scenarios in which a future Soviet aggressor might see the subtle pressure of a blockade of Europe as more effective and much less risky than an armoured onslaught across the North German plain, particularly now that the former

Warsaw Pact allies are no longer available to supply troops, bases and transport facilities. A large, modern submarine force is far more capable of Atlantic trade war than the U-boats of earlier wars, while many of the former advantages of the escort forces have diminished.

Political changes in the last two years 1989-90 have been rapid and many are irreversible; in particular, the Warsaw Pact has no effective existence. However, the Soviet Union still has a very large and powerful navy, which is compared with that of NATO in Table 1 below. The figures are for ships in the North Atlantic and seas bordering Europe, exclude French and Spanish forces and relate to 1988, the last year for which consistent data are available.[4]

TABLE 1: SOVIET AND NATO NAVAL FORCES, ATLANTIC AND EUROPE

Category	NATO	Soviet
Surface Forces		
Aircraft carriers, VSTOL carriers	11	–
Kiev class carriers	–	2
Helicopter carriers	6	2
Cruisers	16	22
Destroyers, frigates and corvettes	301	201
Coastal escorts, fast patrol boats	267	586
Amphibious force ships (ocean going)	57	25
Mine warfare vessels	270	330
Submarines		
Ballistic missile	35	44
Attack (nuclear)	68	145
Others	103	69
Maritime Aircraft		
Sea based, including helicopters	832	210
Land based, tactical and support	389	530
Land based, ASW aircraft and helicopters	462	210

[4] Department of Defense, *Soviet Military Power* (Washington, 1988).

Such statistical comparisons are of little direct value as there is first the obvious point that national categories differ both in kind and also in description. More fundamentally, comparisons break down because like rarely fights like at sea, a point which becomes increasingly important in the context of arms limitations treaties. The true balance of destroyers, for example, is not, as it might appear, 310 to 201 in favour of NATO; the numbers must be compared with the number of ships to be protected and the threat to which they may be exposed from hostile aircraft, mines and submarines. In this case, the balance strongly favours the Soviet Union.

The Royal Navy cannot protect reinforcements or trade by itself but only as part of NATO. It is also worth re-emphasising that it is ships or, more precisely, their cargoes, which are to be protected and not mythical sea lanes.

Not all the ships in the table would be available to protect shipping, particularly in the first, vital weeks. In the Eastern Atlantic, the Royal Navy would be required to play the major role in protecting US reinforcements.

The ballistic missile submarine forces and the deterrent strategy will not be discussed here, except for some of the essential supporting activities such as mine countermeasures around the Scottish base. The future SSN fleet will not be discussed either, since security makes worthwhile discussion of the future possibilities almost impossible. It is clear that the matching of numbers, capabilities and resources is a far more difficult problem for SSNs than for the surface fleet which forms the subject of this book.

The Soviet Union is still building numerous modern ships[5] and there is, as yet, no sign of any slowdown in this construction. It may well be that this building rate merely reflects decisions taken a decade or so ago, but it must nevertheless be taken fully into account in any present calculations.

These figures can be examined further to see if there is evidence of slowing down.

Large numbers have been scrapped, but these are vessels such as Whisky class submarines, 30 years old, which have not been to sea for a decade or more.

Even if the present Soviet leaders are sincere in their desire for

---

[5] Department of Defense, *Soviet Military Power* (Washington, 1989).

TABLE 2: SHIPBUILDING 1979-88

	USN	Other NATO	USSR
Major surface warships (over 900 tonnes)	81	94	84
Submarines (all types)	40	29	75

TABLE 3: SOVIET RATE OF BUILDING

Category	Yearly Average Build	
	1982-84	1986-88
Submarine	9	9
Major surface ships	9	9
Minor surface ships	57	55

peace, and it appears that they are, it is far from certain that they will retain their power as the economy declines still further and nationalist fervour grows. A victory for the 'Old Guard' communists is quite possible, as is a military coup, possibly in combination. A victory for the reformers is also possible but such a situation might well provoke a counter-revolution. While Soviet military strength is so great in an area so vital to the West, and its political control is uncertain, the Soviet Union must be seen at least as a potential threat.

The Soviet navy is, of course, not without its own problems. The present Soviet government has now begun to face the reality of the cost of their war machine, and seems determined to reduce such costs. As a land power whose ultimate security cannot be threatened from the sea, the USSR will almost certainly choose to make cuts in spending which will fall most heavily on the navy.

Soviet naval leaders still seem wedded to the strategy of keeping their SSBN force in 'bastions' defended by SSNs and aircraft, close to their own shores. As part of this strategy, submarines and aircraft are required in large numbers to control the Norwegian Sea against the US strike fleet and its 'Maritime Strategy'.[6] While this

---

[6] Norman Friedman, *The US Maritime Strategy* (London, 1988).

policy remains in force there will be few submarines on the trade routes, but this situation could change rapidly. Indeed, extracts published recently from a book by Admiral of the Fleet Vladimir N Chernavin indicate that 'views on the role and place of sea lines of communication in modern war are being reviewed'. Chernavin also observes 'In the event a world war is unleashed, the significance of sea lines of communication to NATO ... will be increased' and that 'maritime shipping is an important factor that impacts the capabilities of NATO countries to maintain their economic and military potential'.[7]

The Soviet navy has many other, lesser problems too, such as the large number of men who cannot speak Russian, a lack of long-service, senior ratings, and unreliable equipment. The loss of the Mike class submarine *Komsomolets* on 7 April 1989 seems to show major problems both in system reliability and in training.[8] Nevertheless, the Soviet navy, including its air component, poses a major potential threat to NATO.

The Atlantic is the most important area for Western or British seapower but not the only one in which vital interests are at stake. As noted above, Europe depends to a very considerable extent on imports of oil from the Middle East; these imports could be shut off at source or choked, possibly using mines, at the Straits of Hormuz, of Bab al Mandab, Suez or in the Mediterranean itself. Most of the states in the Gulf, the Horn of Africa, the Middle and Near East are politically unstable and vulnerable to a greater or less extent to militant takeovers. Some such states are heavily armed, already have a capability for chemical warfare and are approaching a nuclear capability. A number of such states in combination could be an extremely potent force.

The Indian Ocean and the Pacific may seem too far off to be seen as of vital interest to the UK; this was an argument pressed strongly by the Treasury in the 1930s.[9] If nothing else, the UK has a great moral commitment to Australia and New Zealand in the light of their support in two World Wars. The remaining commitment to

---

[7] Quoted in *Warship World*, (Liskeard, Autumn 1990).

[8] William Carley, 'Diary of a Disaster: Last hours of a Soviet Sub' *Sunday Times*, (London, 16 March 1990).

[9] G C Peden, *British Rearmament and the Treasury*, (Edinburgh, 1979).

Hong Kong could still cause serious problems.

Since World War II the Royal Navy has been involved in many demanding and often dangerous operations worldwide. These include wars such as Korea as part of the UN force, Suez and the Falklands, 'confrontations' such as that with Indonesia in defence of Malaysia and, more recently, in the Gulf, and also attempts to bring economic pressure to bear on other countries, as in the Beira blockade of Rhodesia. Politicians of all parties speak of the need to reduce British commitments but, when in power, are quick to use the Navy's capability for rapid intervention or to provide a show of force. Such operations require capabilities from British ships which are irrelevant to a mid-Atlantic war. Care is needed in interpreting the significance of some of the smaller operations. In some, the use of the Navy, because it was available, was significant but the importance of the operation might not, in itself, justify a very expensive fleet. Only the interruption of the all-important supply lines can be seen as truly vital to Britain.

Cuts in funding for all navies seem inevitable. The much-maligned 'Ten-year Rule', introduced by the United Kingdom in 1919[10] seemed very sensible – and still does – and was applied flexibly. Resources will be discussed in the next chapter but the British weakness in 1939 was more due to destruction of vital industries and skills than to a simple shortage of money. Preservation of such 'seed corn' is truly vital.

This book deals with the technical problems of a medium sized navy, and specifically those of ship design, in matching such a navy's tasks and capabilities to its resources in terms of numbers of ships and individual ship capabilities. This is a problem without a solution, but I believe it can be greatly alleviated by the imaginative use of innovative technology.

---

[10] *Ibid.*

2

The Surface Warship

A few years ago the value of the surface warship seemed in doubt, a view strongly expressed in the UK Defence Review of 1981.[1] The frigate was seen as less effective in anti-submarine warfare than either nuclear submarines or maritime patrol aircraft, particularly in the light of the rising real cost of frigates and their support. It was also thought to be excessively vulnerable since one hit from a small, sea-skimming missile like Exocet could disable a frigate, even though it could not usually sink it.

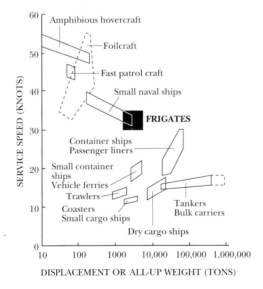

Figure 2/1: Much of this book is about frigates; this diagram shows how frigates compare with other marine vehicles in size and speed.

[1] *The Way Forward: The United Kingdom Defence Programme* (HMSO, London, June 1981) Cmd 8258, commonly referred to as the Nott Report.

The outlook seemed even more gloomy; ocean reconnaissance satellites were increasing in capability using visible light, radar and infra red sensors, and it was likely that by the end of the century they would be capable of monitoring continuously the position of all surface ships, possibly with enough accuracy to guide missiles into homing radius. Quieter Soviet submarines were posing a greater threat and were far more difficult to locate.

The picture looks very different today as the Falklands War, the Armilla patrol in the Gulf and, in a different sense, the collapse of the Warsaw Pact all emphasise the value of controlled application of limited force, an aspect of naval power in which the surface ship excels. Above all, the surface ship can loiter in an area of tension, communicate continuously with its government and take a wide range of actions as thought necessary. Communication does not and should not rely entirely on one system, such as satellites, which may be put out of action, but on a range of modes and frequencies. Clear and rapid communication with other ships and aircraft, with fleet headquarters and with the government is also essential if a major war is to be prevented, scaled down or won.

Surface ships can communicate easily; submarines cannot. There is no indication of any great technological breakthrough in communicating with a submerged submarine and it is likely that if any new physical effect was discovered which made such communication possible, it could also be used to detect the submarine.

A surface ship is versatile and can use controlled force. Its power to influence ranges from showing the flag and cocktail party diplomacy, through gunboat action – the traditional shot across the bows – to a considerable capability in major war. The very visibility of a surface warship is important in giving the impression of latent power and protection and, unlike aircraft, it can remain on station for long periods.

The new generation of quieter Soviet submarines will reduce the effectiveness of passive sonar and force a greater use of active sonar, which cannot readily be used from submarines as such use would disclose their position. Active transmission from the frigate or its helicopters combined with the latter's ability to localise, classify and destroy enemy submarines leads to an enhanced role for the frigate.

Contrary to popular view, the Falklands war also showed that the frigate is not as vulnerable to modern weapons as had been believed, though care is needed in interpreting the lessons of that war, since no effective underwater weapons were used against the task force. The loss of *Sheffield* after being hit by an Exocet is remembered, while the survival of *Glamorgan*, with much of her fighting capability intact, is forgotten. In a later section it will be suggested that the next generation of frigates can be made much more resistant to damage and will truly 'fight hurt'.

Consideration should be given to the survival of the force and not just to that of individual ships. One heavily protected ship may be of less value than a number of ships, individually easily disabled, but which by their number ensure that some will survive. Even at maximum readiness, the Soviet Navy, including its aircraft, will only have a limited number of missile salvoes and is likely to hold many of these back for use against the US strike fleet.[2] In consequence, at the opening of major hostilities at sea, it is likely that NATO will have more frigates at sea than the Soviet Navy has missile salvoes. A similar, though weaker, argument can be applied to submarine launched torpedoes.

This line of argument strongly suggests that there is safety in numbers and that resources should be distributed amongst numerous ships rather than concentrated in a few, powerful vessels. There is also an argument for fighting a new Battle of the Atlantic as far south as possible, lengthening the transit path for Soviet air attack and increasing the vulnerability of the strike aircraft and their tankers to interception.

Historical evidence, discussed below, shows that ships which achieve a good reputation in service are, with a few important exceptions, versatile as designed and adaptable for new tasks during their lives.

The roles of the Royal Navy's surface fleet and the way in which these tasks are carried out are outlined in the remainder of this chapter.

Roles and tasks

The 1981 Defence Review listed Britain's defence roles thus:

---

[2] This consideration was pointed out by Ian Smith in an unpublished talk to The Sir William White Society, Bath.

We have now four main roles: an independent element of strategic and theatre nuclear forces committed to the Alliance; the direct defence of the United Kingdom homeland; a major land and air contribution on the European mainland; and a major maritime effort in the eastern Atlantic and Channel. We also commit home-based forces to the alliance for specialist reinforcement contingencies, particularly on NATO's European flanks. Finally we exploit the flexibility of our forces beyond the NATO area so far as our resources permit, to meet both specific British responsibilities and the growing importance to the West of supporting our friends and contributing to world stability more widely. There can be no question of abandoning our contribution in any of these roles, especially in face of a growing threat.

From this statement one may deduce the roles of the Royal Navy to be:

☐ Operation and protection of the ballistic missile submarine (SS(B)N) force;

☐ Protection of the Home base;

☐ Protection of Britain's vital interests on and beside the sea; and

☐ Provision of an amphibious capability.

These aims still hold, though with some differences in interpretation, but such generalisations do little to guide defence planners; they must therefore be expanded into defined tasks.

The threat to the Home base could be invasion (unlikely though not impossible), or terrorist action against coastal targets or the oil and gas installations offshore on which the economy depends. The threat to the SS(B)N force is real and could come from enemy attack submarines (SSNs), from mines or (possibly) from saboteurs. Detection of SS(B)Ns is difficult and likely to remain so as their pattern of operations is such as to make acoustic detection unlikely. Non-acoustic methods have been tried by most major powers, including the detection of the surface waves generated by a moving body, heat transfer and magnetic anomaly, but all are short-range and effective only in ideal conditions. The mine threat in the Clyde approaches is serious to both US and RN submarines, even though it would only affect one or two boats of the total force.

Protection of vital interests rests on the political will to define a problem as vital. In the past, when there was a large Royal Navy, it was easy for the government to use sea power since it was readily available; now there can be no question of building and maintaining an expensive navy for operations which do not greatly affect the well being of the state. In consequence, historical examples of the protection of vital interests must be used with caution.

Tasks which still seem vital are the protection of military reinforcements across the Atlantic and the protection of essential imports such as oil, food and fertilisers. Reduction in the numbers of US troops stationed in Europe, together with the unstable politics of Eastern Europe, can be seen as increasing the importance of protecting reinforcement shipping. The potential threat from Soviet submarines and naval aircraft, including the use of mines, is serious and shows no sign of diminishing.

The potential threat to Northern Norway remains and the uncertainty over the boundaries of oilfields offshore in that area could still be a cause of conflict. The Soviet Union is concerned, with some justice, that oil installations in that area might support sensors to track aircraft and submarines and electronic monitoring devices. The security of this region is most certainly a vital interest of all NATO powers and also of the Soviet Union.

It is probably in NATO's interest to reduce tension in the Norwegian Sea, an area in which the Soviet Union sees itself as threatened but one in which NATO's interest is primarily defensive. The USN Maritime Strategy[3] can be seen as provocative, envisaging the forward deployment of strike carriers and ships with cruise missiles in this area, all with the capacity for nuclear attack.

Norwegian Sea operations envisage a period of tension during which fairly small British and Netherlands marine contingents would be held offshore, landing when requested by Norway. These forces would then hold or delay the enemy advance until the US Strike Fleet arrives, some ten days later. During this time the whole of the Soviet Northern naval air force, some 400 aircraft, would be opposed by a few RAF Tornados, refuelling in mid-air, and the nine Harriers of one CVS, together with helicopters from the same CVS and, possibly, two aviation support ships. The life of such a force would surely be much less than ten days.

---

[3] N Friedman, *The US Maritime Strategy* (London, 1988).

Outside the NATO area, the UK has commitments to the few remaining British colonial possessions and to some members of the Commonwealth. There is still a dormant threat to the Falklands but the greater threat is a breakdown of negotiations over Hong Kong though, whatever the provocation, it is hard to envisage Britain fighting China over the handover of the colony.

Britain has few other formal commitments in the Pacific area but, in view of the moral commitment to Australia and New Zealand noted in the Introduction, it seems certain that the United Kingdom would assist in the event of a threat to these countries.

The Middle East remains in turmoil and it is an area with many British interests, both political and economic. The Armilla patrol and, even more, British support for Kuwait, have shown that the British government is prepared to take considerable risks in defence of British shipping in the area and that military support might well be given to friendly states if they are attacked. Many of the nations in the area have considerable numbers of modern weapons systems, including aircraft, and a good deal of experience in their wartime operation. Trade routes, particularly in the Gulf, are susceptible to mining and it would be unwise to expect any future lay to be confined to the small and simple contact mines which caused so much damage to the USS *Samuel B Roberts*, particularly in the light of the very sophisticated mines laid by Libya in the Red Sea in 1983 and damage to USS *Princeton* and USS *Tripoli* in the Gulf War.

Piracy,[4] deliberate pollution and other such crimes are a matter for a UN police force rather than unilateral naval action, though until such a force is created, minor action may be justified.[5]

Britain's security depends on the ability to use the Atlantic supply routes and, to a slightly lesser extent, routes to and through the Middle East. These are the vital interests which justify a strong Royal Navy; all else is secondary.

Trade protection

Both the Soviet and NATO navies have a choice of strategies. The

---

[4] R Villar, *Piracy Today* (London, 1985).
[5] J Cable, *Gunboat Diplomacy 1919-1979* (Basingstoke, 1981).

Soviet Union can hold back most of its submarines to protect the SS(B)N sanctuaries and the Kola area against the US Strike Fleet, leaving only a few to attack reinforcement ships. There seems no doubt that this has been the Soviet navy's preferred strategy to date and there are only slight indications that it is about to change. On the other hand, the USSR has the potential to conduct a major submarine offensive in mid Atlantic and, in war, potential threats often become real, particularly since Soviet capability to wage a land war is so much reduced by the loss of Warsaw pact support.

NATO can protect its supplies either using the traditional and successful strategy of escorted convoys or by destroying submarines in barrier operations at choke points, combined with protecting sea lanes of communication. Various intermediate strategies are also possible. In all previous wars, even in the sailing ship era, convoy has proved the cheapest and best strategy. In World War I the introduction of convoys, even with an inadequate number of escorts and with no effective means of detecting a submerged submarine, led to a dramatic fall in the number of sinkings.[6]

In World War II, convoys were introduced from the start and again proved very successful, a lesson relearnt by the US Navy off the American coast in 1942 and even later by the Japanese in the Pacific. Losses of ships in convoy were much less than ships sailing independently on the same route; a ratio of at least 1:3 was common. Since most of the independents were faster ships, the benefit of convoy, on equal terms, was even greater. It seems strange that it is now proposed to abandon the convoy strategy which has always worked in favour of hunting groups, patrolling mythical sea lanes, which has never worked.

Two factors tended to change opinion on convoys in the early year after World War II. One was the success of hunting groups, particularly when formed around an escort carrier. Such groups from the US Navy sank fifty-four U-boats, all but one of which were first located by ULTRA code breaking. Of the total, half were sunk while the group was acting in a convoy escort role.[7] It seems unlikely that code breaking will be operationally significant in the future.

The other problem for convoys was the introduction of nuclear

---

[6] V E Tarrant, *The U-Boat Offensive 1914-1945* (London, 1989).
[7] J S Breemer, 'Defeating the Submarine – Choosing the ASW Strategy' *Naval Forces* IX (1988).

weapons. At conventional spacing a convoy could be wiped out by a single weapon, yet if ships were spaced to minimise losses from such weapons, the perimeter would be so lengthy that a prohibitive number of escorts would be needed. Today, it seems much less likely that nuclear weapons will be used, particularly in a trade war, as noted in the Introduction.

In the last two submarine wars the advantages of convoys can be summarised as follows:[8]

☐ A convoy was little more likely to be located than a single ship and hence even unescorted convoys were safer than single ships. This was used to dispel arguments that there were or are too few escorts for safe convoying.

☐ Escorts reduced losses to merchant ships and increased the number of submarines destroyed. The attacking U-boats were forced to seek their victims where protection was greatest.

☐ Large convoys were safer than small ones since the perimeter increases only as the square root of the number of ships, and hence escort vessels are more closely spaced. In an operational research study of convoys in 1941-2 it was shown that smaller convoys (average size 32 ships) lost 2.5 percent while bigger convoys (average 54 ships) lost 1.1 percent.

☐ Convoys would be given air support. Not only did aircraft sink many submarines, but they were particularly effective in forcing submarines to submerge. On the surface, U-boats had a speed of about 18 knots, twice the speed of any convoy, while submerged speed, except for a short sprint, was about 4 to 5 knots, much slower than the convoy. The presence of aircraft destroyed the mobility advantage of submarines over their target. The use of small airships by the Royal Navy in World War I should have made this lesson clear.[9]

☐ Finally, the routing of convoys could respond effectively to electronic intelligence. While code breaking was the most valu-

---

[8] M B Wignall, The Convoy System: Retrospect and Prospect, *Journal of Naval Science* Vol 9, 1-3 (1983). These articles, originally classified, can now be consulted at the Imperial War Museum and the Ministry of Defence Library. I am grateful to the editor for permission to use this material.
[9] Patrick Abbott, *The British Airship at War 1914-1918* (Lavenham, 1989).

able procedure, it was found that direction finding and the pattern of radio messages gave quite a good picture of German dispositions even when their codes could not be broken. The information deduced when codes could not be broken was sufficient for evasive routing of convoys but was not sufficiently precise to direct hunting groups.

In recent years all these advantages have been eroded by developments in technology:

☐ Reconnaissance satellites are now, or soon will be, able to track either convoys or individual ships continuously.

☐ The speed of the convoy is much less than the submerged speed of submarines. Merely forcing the boat down is of no value. The relative speed of the escort has changed little if one interprets escort as a helicopter with a speed of about 100 knots or 40-50 knots allowing time to hover and listen.

☐ The use of submarine-launched cruise missiles enables attacks to be made at much greater range, increasing the perimeter to be protected. The number of missiles carried is, however, quite limited and the longest ranges depend on aircraft guidance. The longer range of the weapon is at least partially balanced by the great improvement in the range of sonars since the war. It is assumed that nuclear tipped missiles are unlikely to be used at sea, partly from fear of escalation and partly because nuclear anti-submarine weapons tip the balance in favour of NATO.

Advantage in war is rarely permanent and much of the value of convoys will be restored if reconnaissance satellites can be destroyed quickly and reliably. The speed advantage of merchant ships over submerged submarines is most unlikely to be restored but much can be done to reduce the threat from missiles. In trade warfare, it remains true that the attacker must come to the convoy which is, therefore, both bait and trap.

By routing convoys well south, on the latitude of the Azores, NATO planners can ensure that Soviet aircraft will have a long and hazardous two-way flight from their bases; it can be assumed that any Bears based in Cuba or Africa will be taken out very quickly. There is still a clear advantage in having VSTOL fighters with the convoy and, since small carriers are scarce, this is another argument for large convoys.

So far this section has largely been concerned with the submarine threat to trade, but the Soviet Naval Air Force also has the capability for devastating strikes against shipping. There can be no absolute defence against such a strike by a number of Backfires, but much can be done to make it costly and therefore rare. The southern strategy, outlined in the previous paragraph, would make it essential for attacking aircraft to refuel, possibly on both legs of the sortie. Such mid-air refuelling would take place in areas within range of NATO shore-based fighters and the rate of attrition of both bombers and their tankers would be high. It is unlikely that the convoy escorts, even if they included a few Harriers, would destroy many attacking aircraft, but a combination of decoys and local area defence missiles should reduce the number of missiles which hit.

There are other consequences of a southern strategy. In these calmer waters ship motions will be reduced and hence the availability of helicopters will be increased; the effectiveness of sonars, particularly those hull mounted, will also be enhanced.

Anti-submarine operations by SSNs in the Greenland-Iceland area may still be valuable, making the recent reductions in the Royal Navy's SSN force even more regrettable. However, if the Soviet Union should decide to launch an aggressive war on shipping, it is likely that most submarines would have passed the barriers before fighting started. A purely maritime war might well be protracted, forcing submarines to pass and re-pass the barrier as they replenish their missiles. In such a war, it can be assumed that the Soviets would plan to disable the SOSUS seabed installations and destroy the T-AGOS towed array ships or their satellite communications.

It would not be practical for British surface forces based around an *Invincible* to operate in the Greenland gap, at least until the US Strike Fleet had won the battle of the Norwegian Sea. The Gap should be left to NATO SSNs, using their own towed arrays for detection; this approach is aided by the Southern strategy since the submarines would be free of the fear of accidentally sinking friendly surface craft.

The sea lanes from the USA to Europe are some 3000 miles long. Neither maritime patrol aircraft nor frigates are available to protect such lanes throughout their length. Escorts should be concentrated where they are needed, where the attacking submarines are to be found, close to convoys of merchant ships. The southerly route, noted above as a precaution against direct air attack, would also reduce the ability of Soviet aircraft to provide mid-course guidance to long range, submarine-launched missiles. 'Barriers' in the Greenland–Iceland area should be left to NATO SSNs.

The submarine threat from other navies remains a less serious problem. While a number of navies operate modern diesel-electric submarines of considerable capability, at least on paper, experience in both world wars, in all navies, showed how much the success of a submarine attack depends upon the skill, experience and mental toughness of the commanding officer. These qualities are difficult to nurture in the smaller navies due to lack of realistic exercise.[10]

Anti-aircraft warfare (AAW)

The defence of a convoy or task force against a determined air attack is not easy and it is generally accepted that only a multi-layered defence will succeed in stopping a high proportion of attackers. Ideally, defence starts with a pre-emptive strike against the aggressor's bases, a task for which the Royal Navy's abortive carrier, CVA-01, was designed and, since that programme was cancelled in 1967, such a strike is not now possible for the Royal Navy.[11] The next step is to detect the raid at long range from Airborne Early Warning aircraft (AEW), which can vector in fighters, first those armed with long-range missiles, such as the Phoenix, and then others with medium-range missiles.

The range at which aircraft launch their anti-ship missiles is so great that the ships', own missiles must be seen as anti-missile rather than anti-aircraft. This, too, has been thought of as a two-stage defence, with medium-range area-defence missiles and a close-in weapon system which may be either guns or missiles. It is increasingly doubtful whether an area-defence missile can be effective against sea-skimming and 'pop-up' incoming missiles and an extended range, point-defence system,[12] with some ability against

---

[10] D K Brown, 'The Technology of Submarine Design' *Interdisciplinary Sciences Review* vol 15/3 (1990).

[11] D K Brown, *A Century of Naval Construction* (London, 1983).

[12] N Friedman, *World Naval Weapon Systems* (Annapolis, 1989).

crossing targets, may be the only possible approach. There is a saying that a point-defence missile system exists to defend a point which would not need defending if the system were not there: self-defence is important, but it is not what the ship is there for.

The reality for the Royal Navy is very different; there are no big carriers and hence no true fighters outside the range of shore based planes, and these may not be available in the light of their many other commitments. The RAF's contribution to defending a force in the Norwegian Sea will be Tornado ADVs, each of which will need to be re-fuelled several times in transit to the operational area; such support will clearly be few in numbers and rapid reinforcement will be impossible. Control by the AWACS AEW aircraft will greatly improve the effectiveness of both the Tornados and the nine Harriers from a CVS while the force is operating under their cover. The Harrier's success in the Falklands was largely due to the performance of the Sidewinder AIM-7 missile and to the tactical skill of the Task Force Commander in ensuring that they only engaged the enemy at the limit of the latter's range, leaving the Argentinian pilots little freedom to manoeuvre or counter-attack.

The air-defence weakness of the Royal Navy would be particularly dangerous should it become involved in independent operations against any of the small, well-equipped military powers, such as some Middle East countries. For example the RN force in the Gulf must rely on the twelve RAF Tornados or on the US Navy for fighter cover. It is not possible completely to remedy this weakness within any credible budget, but there are palliative measures which can be taken.

One carrier is of little value and it is likely that, allowing for refits, the minimum force is three. A section below deals with the formidable design problems of 'cheap' carriers, fighters seems worth more detailed study.

The best available missile system is the AEGIS,[13] based on the SPY-1 planar array radar and the SM-2 missile in its latest form. The system itself is very expensive and needs a ship of about 8000 tonnes (deep). USS *Ticonderoga* costs about $300 million more than USS *Spruance*, and this must be largely due to the cost of AEGIS. This system seems to have been rejected in Britain on cost grounds, and

[13] *Ibid.*

the British government has renewed its commitment to the FAAMS missile project. The FAAMS project should provide local air defence, while developments of the Sea Wolf should be effective in close protection for many years to come.

FAAMS, the Family of Anti-Aircraft Missiles, is being developed by France, Italy, Spain and the United Kingdom. The missile is based on the French Aster and, initially, will provide a local area system for the UK and Spain, and point defence for France and Italy, and will later be developed as a medium-range system. The vertically launched missile will have a very high acceleration and will be directed by a phased array under development by Marconi and Selenia.[14]

Evidence of the continuing value of guns is conflicting; despite press reports, guns were of very little value in defending the Falklands ships. Most of the guns available, however, were of World War II vintage, in small numbers, used against jet aircraft of the 1950s. The gun is important to the morale of the crew (and this factor probably justifies some investment) and guns do have some deterrent effect against attack by manned aircraft.

A ship needs to detect a sea-skimming missile very quickly if it is to take effective counter measures with either decoys or weapons. The airship or even the kite balloon, towed behind ships in both World Wars, could provide a cheap platform for a large radar, extending the horizon, and it could also deploy decoys.

Anti-submarine warfare (ASW) – tactics and weapons

The strategy of ASW and the choice between a convoy strategy and protected sealanes has been discussed above. Whichever strategy is adopted, the enemy submarine has to be located, classified and destroyed.

For many years, the US Navy's SOSUS system has been the primary early warning system in the North Atlantic. Fixed hydrophone arrays can detect the radiated noise from submarines at very long range, alerting shoreside operations rooms. Because these installations are fixed, they are vulnerable to counter measures and they cannot be redeployed to meet threats in other parts of the world.

---

[14] *Ibid.*

Very long passive arrays, towed slowly by T-AGOS vessels, have some mobility and hence slightly reduced vulnerability. Their data, however, are transmitted for analysis ashore over satellite channels which themselves are vulnerable to disruption. It is understood that the motion of these ships at their very low operating speeds is intolerable and hence from T-AGOS 19 they will be SWATHs (Small Waterplane Area Twin Hull), giving reduced motions; see Appendix 1.

Sonobuoy barriers, laid by patrol aircraft or ships' helicopters, overcome some of these problems, but sonobuoys are not cheap and, since barriers will require frequent renewal, will be required in very large numbers. Shortage of sonobouys could soon become a problem in a prolonged war, as would numbers of patrol aircraft, since the RAF has only about twenty-eight Nimrods and it probably needs four to five to keep one on station. Frigates and SSNs deploy sonar arrays which have proved capable of detecting current submarines at long range.

All the sonars mentioned above detect the sound radiated by submarines and, in recent years, the Soviet Navy has introduced new classes of much quieter boats. Machinery has been designed to generate less noise and mounted to attenuate what is produced, propellers have been developed to produce smaller and less recognisable pressure fluctuations in the sea and the hull has been coated with flexible tiles, further reducing sound levels. Even the best Soviet submarines are still considerably more noisy than those of the Royal Navy, but the gap is narrowing rapidly.

The range at which passive sonars of all sorts can detect these new, quiet submarines is much reduced, though many older, clanking boats will remain in service for years. Though even the new boats can be heard, the shorter range of detection means that many more sensors will be required to form a barrier or a convoy screen.

Active sonar will have a greater part to play, though it, too, has problems. Conventional active sonar discloses the position of the user at greater ranges than those at which it detects an echo, making its use unattractive to submarines. Since active sonar has to detect an echo, inherently weak, from the target, its range is limited and may be further reduced if the target submarine is given an anechoic coating.

There is some advantage in using bi-static active sonar, in which the transmitter and receiver are widely separated.[15] The transmitting ship can be in a safe area, well protected, and emitting very high energy pulses from a transducer in a towed body which may weigh up to 50 tonnes.[16] The target echo can be picked up by receivers, possibly including existing towed arrays, well away and towed from a ship which is quiet.

The characteristics of sound propagation in shallow water are such that conventional active sonars will probably still be needed, and such sets may have a role to play in localising and classifying contacts made at longer range. Non-acoustic detection methods, particularly magnetic anomaly (MAD), will also be useful in shallow waters and for localisation. It seems possible that developments in super-conducting materials may enhance the performance of MAD and other sensors.

Once located and classified as hostile, the submarine must be destroyed. In my view, the use of nuclear weapons at sea would be so likely to escalate to a major nuclear exchange that such use is unthinkable, leaving torpedoes as the main ASW weapon for both ships and aircraft. The light-weight torpedo is usually dropped from helicopters, though it can be discharged from ships via torpedo tubes, or projected to long range by weapons such as Ikara or Subroc. Such torpedoes use active sonar to home on to the target. The US Navy's Mk 46 weighs 258kg and has a range of 11,000 metres at 48 knots at shallow setting.[17] The performance of the British Stingray has not been disclosed but is said to be considerably superior.

The warhead of a lightweight torpedo is inevitably small, and it is sometimes claimed that the double hull and subdivision of Soviet submarines render them safe against such weapons. This seems unlikely, except possibly for the giant Typhoons.[18] Shock damage would in any case be severe, the chance of at least a small hole is high, and a submarine with one compartment flooded would be unable to fight and would face great difficulties in getting home. A submarine damaged by such a torpedo would become an easy tar-

---

[15] C C F Adcock, 'Some Aspects of Bistatic Sonar', *Naval Forces* Vol X (1989).

[16] M Evans, 'Navy Homing in on Silenced Submarines', *The Times* (London, 26 December 1984).

[17] Friedman, *op cit* (n12).

[18] Published accounts of the loss of the Soviet Mike class submarine suggest that their watertight integrity is not good: *Sunday Times* (London, 16 March 1990).

get for a second attack.

Heavyweight torpedoes such as the US Navy Mk 48 and the British Tigerfish, to be replaced by the vastly superior Spearfish, are almost always launched from SSNs and are usually wire-guided to the vicinity of the target, from which range they home using active sonar. They are very fast – 55 knots is quoted for the US Navy's Mk 48 – and have a large enough warhead to destroy any potential target.

The helicopter was originally introduced in the Royal Navy as a weapon delivery system; it would be guided to the vicinity of the target by the parent ship's hull-mounted sonar to release a torpedo. With some modification, this procedure applies to operations with the Lynx today. The bigger Sea King and the new, and even bigger, Merlin (EH 101) can carry sonar buoys, dunking sonar and weapons. They therefore form autonomous weapon systems, though the frigate's towed array may well still be required to make the initial detection. Remote piloted vehicles (RPVs) are far from providing this capability, though they can be used as a weapon delivery system. Anti-submarine warfare depends to a very great extent on helicopters and a central theme of this book will be the need to maximise the number at sea within a limited budget.

To some extent, the shore based maritime patrol aircraft is an alternative to the helicopter. The aircraft are very expensive and about five are needed to ensure that one is on station. Since these aircraft cannot hover, they are, unlike helicopters, unable to use sonar, though they can remain on station much longer. They have a very impressive control and communications fit.

In many ASW operations, a helicopter or patrol aircraft will be required to fly low and slow, which makes either very vulnerable to even the simplest of submarine-launched anti-aircraft missiles. If such missiles were introduced, ASW aircraft would be forced to fly higher and faster and to devote part of their payload to decoys. It is surprising that more attention has not been given to such weapons as, even if they had a low success rate, their use would seriously disrupt ASW operations as currently conducted.[19]

---

[19] Friedman, *op cit* (n12) page 183, gives details of the Ford Aerospace SIAM (Self-Initiated Anti-Aircraft Missile) system for submarines, tested successfully in 1981.

Anti-surface vessel warfare (ASVW)

Though the Soviet Union has a number of very powerful surface warships, it does not seem likely that Royal Navy surface warships would be the appropriate counter to any threat which they might pose to Atlantic shipping. The remaining nuclear submarines, assisted, if these are available, by the RAF's strike aircraft, would be a much more effective solution.

Some potentially hostile countries operate fast attack craft with a powerful anti-surface missile armament. This threat is well countered by Harriers or helicopters using Sea Skua missiles. Present RPVs are probably of most value in giving an over-the-horizon capability to ship-launched missiles. The vulnerability of fast craft to air attack was first demonstrated as early as August 1918, when twelve German seaplanes destroyed or disabled six British coastal motor boats off the Zuider Zee. Though some fast attack craft carry an impressive fit of anti-aircraft weapons, they are too small to support the sophisticated sensors and controls necessary to make these effective.

There is a good case in police operations for a small, very accurate gun which can deliver the traditional shot across the bows without danger of inadvertently hitting the intruding vessel, and which can also guarantee a first round kill against terrorist launches; a high rate of fire is not needed. The Royal Ordnance Factory 105mm, derived from the Centurion tank, is readily available, its ammunition can be found worldwide and the gun, complete with stabilised mounting, is cheap.[20]

It is often argued that a fairly large gun is needed for shore bombardment and that this requirement was demonstrated in the Falklands war. Prior to the British landings, Royal Navy ships fired some 1500 rounds (32½ tons) compared with 30 tons of bombs from Harriers and 21 tons from two inaccurate Vulcan sorties. During the whole campaign 8000 rounds were fired; *Avenger* alone fired 1000 rounds, a tribute to the RARDE who designed the 4.5in Mk 8 barrel. Some bombardments were very accurate: *Ardent* destroyed a Pukara at Goose Green airfield using 20 rounds at 20,000 metres, and *Arrow*'s firing in support of 2nd Para on 28 May

[20] *Ibid.*

was said to have had 'devastating effect'.[21] Many other firings were diversions or were intended to keep Argentine heads down.

However, when the 8000 rounds fired during the whole war is compared with the 10,000 rounds per hour fired during preparation for the Somme offensive in 1916 on a similar area, one may well wonder if naval gunfire support is over-rated. If required, a bolt-on bombardment rocket fit may be more cost effective.

Mine countermeasures (MCM)

There are many problems in evaluating the magnitude of the mine threat. The Soviet Union is said to possess some 225,000 mines, [22] many of which are old fashioned but quite effective, at least in defensive operations. The USSR has the ability to lay mines in NATO waters from submarines, from aircraft and by covert means. However, all such minelaying vehicles will have other tasks as war approaches and in the early days of actual combat. It is not clear what priority will be given to minelaying, but the disruption caused by even a few mines can be very great, as shown during the Iran-Iraq war, and during the more recent Gulf War.

In UK waters the prime MCM task is seen as protecting the British and US SSBN force on passage through the Clyde estuary and out to deep water. Some parts of this route are very confined, for example the Rhu Narrows, and could be mined by two swimmers with breathing apparatus and a lorry; other parts could be mined from disguised merchant ships. Since a very large number of MCM vessels are needed to search for mines over the present long passage in shallow water, the cheapest and most effective protection for the deterrent force might be to move their base to the Outer Hebrides, close to deep water.[23] Since there will be, at most, one British and one USN submarine fully armed in the Clyde and these could fire from their berths, it may well be that undue importance is attached to this MCM task.

Second priority is the protection of the reinforcement routes for

---

[21] J D Brown, *The Royal Navy and the Falklands War* (London, 1987).

[22] M Vego, 'Soviet Navy Mines and their Platforms', *Navy International* (July 1986).

[23] This was written before the closure of the US base in the Clyde was announced.

US troop convoys up the Channel, or at least to French Atlantic ports, and the British Army routes across the North Sea. Most of these routes are shallow and the main threat is from ground mines. The bottom is generally uneven, in many areas tidal currents change the bottom contours frequently and there is a great deal of debris which will confuse the hunter.

Finally, there is a worldwide threat, shown by the Gulf War and the mining of the Red Sea in 1983 by the Libyan ship *Ghat*. In the latter case, sophisticated mines were used which were very difficult to clear. In the Gulf War, horned contact mines were used (the Soviet M-08 model, a type familiar from World War I), but proved their effectiveness by the severe damage to USS *Samuel B Roberts*. Such mines are easy to sweep, but many modern MCM craft are pure hunters with no sweeping capability. Moored mines are not easy to hunt with sonar as they pose a three-dimensional problem rather than the two-dimensional search for a mine on the bottom; the most modern sonars do, however, have some capability for such searches. In worldwide MCM operations, the low transit speed of current MCMVs is a serious problem, and though fast MCMVs are possible, they would be expensive.

Moored mines can be more effective with antennae fuses as in the US Navy's contribution to the Northern Barrage in World War I,[24] or they can have magnetic or acoustic fuses. The US Captor mine fires a Mk 46 torpedo at a submarine heard in the vicinity, while the Soviet Cluster Bay rising mine is rocket-driven to the vicinity of its target.[25] Ground mines rely on influence from a ship's magnetic, acoustic or pressure signatures or, more often, on a combination of such influences. It is quite possible using a small processor to make them sensitive to a specific signature pattern, such as that of an SSBN. In general, any mine with a pressure sensor is unsweepable, while clever acoustic/magnetic combination firing devices will foil most sweeps, and certainly those deployed from helicopters. On the other hand, there are a very large number of simple influence mines in service which can be swept quite easily.

Sweeping moored mines has not changes in principle since World War I, and uses a wire to guide the mine's mooring cable

---

[24] H C Armstrong, 'The Removal of the North Sea Mine Barrage', *Warship International* 2 (1986).

[25] Vego, *op cit*.

into a cutter, so that the mine will float to the surface for destruction. To achieve this result in deep water, close to the bottom, requires a very refined version of the wire sweep. It is assumed that deepwater mines will be targeted against submarines, and hence sweepers can be unsophisticated craft like the Royal Navy's River class. A few anti-MCM mines can, however, cause disruption to mine clearance. It is surprising that the paravane, which gives very effective self protection against moored mines, has not been reintroduced, though it would require modification to be used from ships with bow sonars (a paravane could possibly be towed from a bowsprit).

Magnetic and acoustic sweeps simulate the signature of a ship in the water, well clear of the sweeper, with great precision. Since the sweeper will pass over the mine, its own signatures must be well below any likely mine setting, and the safe level depends on operating depth. Vessels required to support amphibious operations in shallow water will require exceptionally low signatures.

Mine hunting is usually carried out using a high-definition sonar; the success rate is low except on the smoothest of bottoms and multiple passes are needed to get an acceptable rate of detection. A suspicious object will usually have to be examined from several directions before it can be identified as a mine, again slowing the search rate. This procedure also implies a high probability that the hunter will pass over an active mine, so they, too, need low signatures. Once a mine is found and identified, a remote controlled mini-sub will place a charge against the mine to destroy it. Exceptionally, a new type of mine may be recovered and dismantled, a task often made very dangerous, though not impossible, by booby traps. Mines camouflaged with anechoic coatings and shaped to look like rocks can be very difficult to find with sonar, and mines dropped with a high enough velocity to bury themselves in the sea bed are almost impossible to hunt.

There are other approaches to countering the mine threat. During World War II, a constant watch was kept on the approach to British harbours, giving visual indication of mine laying and, by cross bearings, a fair indication of the position of the mine. An even more positive indication was given of mine laying from the air in the Suez Canal as during the night a net was pulled across and any holes found in the morning were likely to indicate a mine below. In narrow channels it should be possible to set up an electronic monitoring system to detect air-laid mines.

Route surveillance is an alternative procedure, in which the object is to monitor selected passages at frequent intervals to ensure that nothing new has appeared on the bottom, using a computer to compare the current sonar picture with the previous one. Clearly, this approach can only be used where the sea bed is smooth, hard and stable, but under these conditions the search can be carried out at high speed, say 20 knots, using side-scan sonar.

Even a small number of mines can require an immense effect to counter and the problem becomes even more difficult if the firing devices are varied and a few anti-MCM devices are scattered amongst them. Even in World War II mines were used with clocks which activated them days after they were laid or with counters so that they would ignore the first few influences, making them hard to sweep.

MCM operations are highly complex and require large numbers of craft. With a few exceptions, all current sweeping and hunting techniques need very sophisticated craft with low pressure, acoustic and magnetic signatures. Such vessels are costly (£30-40 million for a Hunt class), conflicting with the need for numbers. Even if simple craft could be used, the vast fleets of fishing vessels used in two World Wars no longer exist. At the last count there were about twelve deep water trawlers under the British flag, together with about the same number of oil rig support vessels.

Mines are easy to make and lay and they are anonymous. Even a sophisticated firing mechanism is within the scope of a terrorist organisation, let alone a maverick government. Mine warfare is likely to remain a major area of operations for the foreseeable future.

Amphibious operations

The main roles for the Royal Navy's amphibious force can be seen as:

☐ Support for NATO's northern flank;

☐ Worldwide operations in support of national and United Nations policy; and

☐ Relief and rescue.

Of these, only the first can be seem as a truly vital British interest; the use of the force elsewhere may be welcome but such use alone would not justify the high cost of ownership.

The 1986 Statement on the Defence Estimates said that the force was available to reinforce Norway, the Baltic approaches or certain Atlantic islands. The threat to northern Norway is both the greatest and most difficult to counter using other NATO forces such as the ACE Mobile Force, particularly due to the lack of airfields in this area. The potential threat to the NATO northern flank from Soviet forces in the Kola Peninsula is variously reported and probably changing, but in 1989 Soviet units in this area comprised two motorised infantry divisions, one mobilisation division, one missile brigade, one naval infantry brigade and one airborne battalion, together with a very powerful naval air force.

The NATO forces immediately available include the two battalions of Norwegian troops stationed there, plus the UK 3rd Marine Commando Brigade and a Netherlands brigade, both of which could arrive quite quickly. After some time, about twenty days, the Canadian Air/Sea Transportable Brigade could arrive and, in the same time scale, a US Marine Brigade, though the latter is not firmly committed to this role.

If the Soviet Union was determined to occupy northern Norway, the Anglo-Netherlands force could do little to deter or prevent it, but their presence might stop an opportunist attack, which is not inconceivable in the death throes of the current Soviet communist system. Norway does not accept foreign troops permanently based on her soil in peacetime and hence it is envisaged that the amphibious force will require the capability to loiter offshore for a period of weeks, during a time of tension, to be available for a landing on request. There is clearly a considerable element of risk in this aspect of the operation as a full scale Soviet assault could well be preceded by the destruction of the ships of the amphibious force by land-based aircraft or submarines. Since the only air defence is likely to be nine Harriers, the air threat is deadly.

The force is capable of landing directly from its ships over beaches without the use of ports or airfields, both scarce in the north of Norway. The Marines will rely heavily on helicopters and landing craft for mobility, which makes the force 'particularly suitable for operations in northern Norway, where land movement is severely restricted by fjords, poor roads, steep-sided valleys, bridges, defiles and tunnels, and where airfields are few and far between'.[26]

The Allied force exercises annually in the north and is highly trained in such operations. The Anglo-Netherlands force can only deter, or at worst delay, an aggressor and would need major reinforcement at an early stage. It does have advantages; as Liddell Hart pointed out in his widely quoted, though not entirely convincing, paper of 1960,[27]

> Amphibious flexibility is the greatest strategic asset that a sea-based power possesses. It creates a distraction to a continental enemy's concentration that is most advantageously disproportionate to the resources employed.

Outside the NATO area, the UK force could be used if Argentina repeated its occupation of the Falklands, or in Hong Kong if problems arose with China over the handover (though mainly for evacuation), and possibly in other trouble spots. Australia and New Zealand might also require UK assistance in dealing with possible threats. The future in Europe remains uncertain and troubled, enhancing the value of the flexibility of an amphibious force. Such a force can stay poised for long periods without presenting too aggressive a stance, as in 1967 when *Albion* with 41 Commando lay off the Nigerian coast for six weeks during the civil war as a potential aid to British citizens. Relief and rescue following disaster is an historic task for the Royal Navy but would not, in itself, justify the cost of the force.

An amphibious force does not require over-flying rights as would an air-transportable force, and is independent of both ports and airfields. On the other hand, it is expensive. The RN force has one strong brigade of troops and supporting arms which, for its transport, will require two aviation support ships, two assault ships (LPDs) and six LSLs, costing some £1000 million, as well as some requisitioned merchant ships. In addition, it will need a strong

---

[26] Statement on the Defence Estimates (HMSO, London, 1986).

[27] B H Liddell Hart, 'The Value of Amphibious Flexibility and Forces', *Journal RUSI* (November 1960); see also:

J J Mearsheimer, *Liddell Hart and the Weight of History* (New York, 1988). This is a very critical review of Liddell Hart's thinking.

escort, including a CVS if air support is to be provided. The mine threat to landing operations is high and, in most cases, the amphibious force would need a number of MCMVs, at least some of which should be able to sweep in shallow water as well as to hunt mines. If there is a surface threat, support from SSNs will be needed. Such a force is clearly vulnerable; the Falklands could not have been recovered had either of the CVSs been disabled or had there been serious damage to the amphibious force and laden transports. Operations on NATO's Northern Flank and worldwide expose the Royal Navy's weakness in AAW.

Finally, it should not be assumed that amphibious operations are the sole prerogative of NATO. The Soviet Union has a very strong force of ships, hovercraft, helicopters and naval infantry well trained in amphibious work. Even in Norway it should not lightly be assumed that the sea, let alone the air, is NATO controlled. Clancy's fictional World War III[28] shows the vulnerability of Iceland to assault and the dangerous consequences to NATO which would ensue. The Faroes, Shetlands and possibly the Azores could also be open to attack, while the threat to the Baltic approaches is well known. Some Middle Eastern countries, such as Iraq and Iran, also have amphibious capability, including hovercraft.

Coast guard

There are also a number of duties traditionally carried out by the Royal Navy which have little connection with defence. There are advantages, and some disadvantages, in separating the control, funding and manning of such tasks from the Navy and establishing a Coastguard service on the lines of that in the USA. Such a service would take over the following naval duties:

☐ Offshore protection

☐ Hydrography and related oceanographic studies

☐ Co-ordination of disaster relief and rescue in UK waters

This new Coastguard would clearly absorb the existing coastguards and their duties. It should also have operational control

---

[28] See n2 in the Introduction, above.

over the activities of Trinity House and the Royal National Lifeboat Institution, though since these organisations work well, they should preserve a considerable measure of independence; a joint Board of Directors might be an appropriate solution. It would also be desirable to include the Scottish Fishery protection service and the Northern Lights in such a combined service but the Irish Lights, which deals with both Eire and Ulster, would obviously present political problems. This new service would also control pollution of the sea and, like the US Coastguard, carry out the regulatory work for ships of the Department of Transport.

Such an organisation, independent of the Navy, would make clear to Parliament and to the public what funds are available for maritime defence and what is required for ancillary services. The Coastguard would also be able to recruit personnel from a wider range of the population than the Navy; as in the US Coastguard, women could be recruited in some numbers for seagoing duties and some men, reluctant to undertake military duties, might wish to join a mainly humanitarian organisation.

The vessels available to the proposed Coastguard would include: (for fishery protection) two Castle class, seven Island class, five Scottish vessels (roughly equivalent to Island class) and eight smaller Scottish boats; (for the hydrography service) three *Herald/Hecta*

A Castle class OPV with a Sea King helicopter about to land on. Note the position of the bridge, well aft to reduce vertical motions, the high freeboard and the knuckle, both of which help to keep her dry.

class, five *Roebuck/Bulldog* class and one *Gleaner*, and (for the Coastguard) some ten to twelve fast launches.

Of these, only the Castles have any military capability, and this is limited. They are too noisy for anti-submarine work and would need major, and expensive, work if an effective armament was to be fitted. Like the Islands, they do, however, have a very good communications and plotting capability. The Castles additionally have a flight deck suitable for a Sea King (or EH 101) and have even accepted a Chinook.

If the Coastguard were to be considered as a naval reserve, it would have to have the right ships and men trained to operate them in war. The corvettes described in Chapter 7 below would be very effective offshore protection vessels and could easily be converted for survey work. However, such ships would be very much more expensive than those needed for the Coastguard's primary role. The extra cost of such ships would fall on the Naval Budget, so destroying the financial independence seen as a major advantage of a separate service.

Even if suitable ships were deployed, their crews would need very frequent training if they were to use complicated sensors and weapons effectively. The time needed for this training would mean that more ships and crews were needed than for their peacetime role. Such training would also make it difficult, perhaps even impossible, to widen the area of recruiting as suggested above.

It would seem that the US Coastguard is finding it increasingly difficult to maintain its wartime capability for just these reasons. A British Coastguard should not be regarded as a direct Naval Reserve, though in war some of its vessels and personnel might be requisitioned and used. It nevertheless still seems appropriate to separate the non-military duties and costs from the Navy, and there should be considerable advantage to the country in bringing together maritime services devoted to law enforcement, survey, rescue, pollution control and so on. Such a service should be far more capable of coping with a major maritime disaster than the current services.

Police action

There are still many occasions on which the presence of a warship, making a show of force, can defuse a potentially explosive situation;

warships are also needed to prevent piracy. Gunboat diplomacy remains an occasional requirement of governments and, though one would not build and maintain a navy for this specific purpose, all naval vessels should have the capability to exert low-level force: this usually means a small gun. It should be remembered that today's gunboat may be opposed by missile-firing launches, a capability within the reach of terrorists and of many small countries.[29]

[29] Cable, *op cit* (n5).

3

Resources and Constraints

The matching of tasks with available resources lies at the root of most problems faced by all defence forces. No country, least of all a democracy, can spend unlimited sums on defence. With a fixed budget, those responsible for the composition of the navy and for the design of its ships are faced with an inevitable conflict between the need for numbers of ships to meet commitments and the need for optimum capability within individual units, which leads to rapidly rising costs. The problem is similar to that faced by house-holders trying to decide on the right level of insurance to cover a remote but serious risk.

In this century one may recognise three policies developed in response to this problem, though they were usually not stated explicitly. In the earlier years, the design aim was that British ships were to be better individually than those of likely opponents; due to the artificial limits of the Naval Limitation Treaties, it was possible to hold to this as an aim up to 1939, even though it was not always achieved, at least for major categories. In the early postwar years, cost benefit analysis was the deciding factor and cost increases, up to a point, were acceptable if the increase in capability was suffi-cient. More recently, the Government has imposed strict cash limits on individual units, seemingly essential if sufficient numbers are to be procured.

While money is the main resource, there are others such as industrial capability and manpower, all of which are limited to some extent and many of which are declining. Other external fea-tures are better seen as constraints than resources; all will be dis-cussed in this chapter.

The first draft of this book was written in 1988-9, before the col-lapse of the Warsaw Pact and the consequent reductions in defence spending. Breakdowns of expenditure are only available for the ear-lier, higher figures and these have been retained in the tables. In

July 1990 the UK Government announced plans which should lead to a reduction of spending by about 25 percent by 1995, though this decision was followed almost immediately by the Iraqi invasion of Kuwait. The Army will bear the largest cuts and the Navy the smallest. Wherever the information is available, references below are to current plans, and these may change either way as the international scene changes.

Resources

Money The United Kingdom is one of the poorer countries in NATO but her spending on defence is one of the highest, however it is measured, as is her willingness to use the Navy to support United Nations actions. The total defence expenditure in 1988-9 was £17,150 million, the fourth highest in NATO which, expressed as a percentage of Gross National Product, was third highest.[1] The per capita expenditure at £300 was fifth in NATO. Only the USA, with its vast size and wealth, is consistently ahead of the United Kingdom in these measures of defence spending.

Defence accounted for 18 percent of the British Government's total expenditure in 1988-9 and with the lessening of international tension in Europe (though not in the Middle East) leading to increased pressure to cut spending and to improve public services, there will be a major reduction in defence spending; it cannot be assumed that the cuts announced will be the last. Against these limited financial resources, the pressure of a threat increasing in sophistication has been driving up the real cost of all defence equipment by some 7 percent per year.[2]

The total defence budget has to be split in various ways between the three services, between commitments, between men and material and between research and production. The proportion devoted to each of these has been reasonably constant over recent years though the pressure of rising costs against a fixed total must lead to further painful decisions in the near future; this problem is con-

---

[1] *Statement on the Defence Estimates* (London, 1988). This is the latest fully detailed breakdown of expenditure before the July 1990 cuts. New totals are given where available.
[2] Phillip Pugh, *The Cost of Seapower* (London, 1986).

cealed for the time being by delays in ordering major equipment programmes.

TABLE 4: BREAKDOWN OF DEFENCE EXPENDITURE 1988-89[3]

Function	expenditure	Percentage of: servicemen	civilians
Nuclear deterrent	5.6	0.6	1.3
Naval combat forces	12.6	12.2	6.8
European ground theatre	17.6	31.4	14.4
Other army	0.9	4.4	3.4
Air force	17.8	18.8	5.2
Reserves	2.2	0.9	1.8
Research and development	11.7	0.3	13.8
Training	6.5	17.9	7.5
Equipment, support etc in UK	5.0	2.7	21.2
War stocks	2.7	–	–
Other support functions	18.0	10.8	24.6

Strong arguments can be raised, even by a single-minded Navy man, for increasing many of the items in Table 4. For example, the Navy needs more air support, both from long-range, shore-based fighters and from maritime patrol aircraft.

Equipment accounts for 43 percent (£8,240M) of the total budget and, of this, the Navy gets 34 percent (14.7 percent of the total defence budget) or about £2,800 million. The breakdown of the Navy's total vote, £2,425 million, men and material, is shown in Table 5.

Other costs also need to be taken into account in this calculation; these are shown in Table 6.

In addition, the Navy's share of general support functions (£3,526 million) must be considered, along with a few other common services and that part of the Royal Air Force used for maritime operations. Maritime aircraft are listed at £130 million but fighter

---

[3] See note 1

TABLE 5: BREAKDOWN OF NAVAL EXPENDITURE1988-89[4]

	£ million	percentage
Submarines	431	18
Aircraft carriers and ASW carriers	104	4
Amphibious forces	99	4
Destroyers and frigates	660	27
Mine countermeasures vessels	100	4
Other ships	428	18
Aircraft	265	11
Fleet headquarters	117	5
Overseas shore establishments	51	2
Naval bases and operational support	170	7
TOTAL	2425	100

TABLE 6: ADDITIONAL DEFENCE EXPENDITURE 1988-89

	£ million
Reserves	420
Research and development	348
Training	111
Royal Dockyards	955
War stocks	520

and strike support to the fleet is not shown. In passing, one may note that the decision to leave maritime aircraft in the RAF when the Fleet Air Arm was formed, just before World War II, made some sense when many maritime aircraft were the same as those used by Bomber Command, but it makes no sense today. It is incredible to think of a Nimrod attack on a defended shore target.

The breakdowns in the tables above can only be used as a very

[4] See note 1; a partial breakdown for 1989-90 is:

Category	£ million
Submarines	417
Carriers	95
Amphibious ships	109
Destroyers and frigates	641
MCMV	81

rough guide to the way the budget is allocated. There are many real problems in allocating costs to functions; for example, should not the cost of escorts to landing ships appear under amphibious forces rather than frigates? Central support, a vast total, cannot easily be separated, and some areas of research serve all services (for example, electronic countermeasures). Neither should it be forgotten that only a few years ago similar figures were manipulated to conceal the very expensive Chevaline nuclear warhead programme from Parliament, press and people.

The figures indicate the size of funds which were available and how this was divided. The plans announced for the Navy in July 1990 include a frigate force of forty vessels instead of about fifty in earlier years. The immediate effect of this cut will be small as the vessels disposed of will be old, of limited capability and expensive to run. Provision of funds to keep the force of forty ships up to date may be difficult, since during the rundown of the armed forces there will be a large number of fixed costs, some of which, such as retirement payments, will increase, reducing funds for new construction.

However, we may assume here that funds for frigate building will be about 80 percent of the total previously available. In later chapters, suggestions will be made for increases in some figures, but this will be offset against specific reductions elsewhere. Any such changes should be moderate in size and introduced gradually since naval equipment has a such a very long lead time.

Shipbuilding The problem posed by shipbuilding resources is very different; here the problem is one of gross overcapacity. There are some five or six yards capable of building all the ships needed by the Royal Navy surface fleet, at least up to destroyer size, yet one of these yards could provide all the vessels needed, including submarines and small aircraft carriers.

This surplus capacity has been preserved partly to avoid unemployment and partly to ensure that competitive tendering is possible. Such a policy has led to a large number of yards which are undercapitalised and with very limited resources. Most yards have been preserved from closure by management buyouts with limited scope for investment; only two are part of larger groups with possible access to substantial funds. It seems inevitable that most of these yards will either close or move out of frigate building.

The policy of competitive tendering has undoubtedly saved many millions of pounds on the procurement of the current generation of warships but it does not encourage yards to invest in research, nor to maintain design teams or even large drawing offices. All these shipyards are assembly contractors, with some considerable skill in production engineering but very little in design or advanced technology (see Chapter 10). In fact, the United Kingdom as a whole is very short of warship design skill and experience, in all professions, and it seems inevitable that competitive design will lead to a very low-risk solution. Design capability has been reduced within the Ministry of Defence while the procurement policy adopted has prevented industry from building up its own capability; available skills are too thinly spread.

Problems in the naval weapons industry seem to be different but even more serious. Over the years, weapons firms have made large profits and, perhaps, have found life too easy. The failure of the command system on the Type 23 frigate and the long delays in getting the Tigerfish torpedo fit for service are conspicuous. On the other hand, Sea Wolf has been very successful, as has the Stingray torpedo.

Dockyards Until recently there was a deliberate policy of preserving overcapacity in the Royal Dockyards as a war reserve, both in capital equipment and in manpower. The need for such a reserve is said to be less today, though such capacity proved invaluable during the Falklands war (when the Dockyards fitted the majority of helicopter decks, desalination plants and all the other equipment needed on requisitioned merchant ships).

Under the present system of commercial management, overcapacity is impossible, though presumably a contract could be written requiring such a reserve to be provided at an economic rate. Refit work is inherently difficult to plan as more work emerges as the ship is opened up (a problem familiar to car owners facing a garage bill far higher than expected).

The present refit capacity of Rosyth and Devonport Dockyards, plus a refit base at Portsmouth, is adequate and there is still a reserve capacity as regards major equipment, though not of manpower. There is a very limited commercial ship repair industry. In addition there are six Fleet Maintenance Units for routine work and minor repairs. These are naval manned and work costs some

20 percent more than in the Dockyards. They can respond more quickly and are seen by some as insurance against industrial disputes.[5]

Constraints

Manpower In Britain, as in other developed nations, it is clear that there will be far fewer young people on the labour market in coming years. This shortage will mean that young people will have more freedom to choose attractive jobs with good pay and conditions. Difficulty in recruiting already shows that a decreasing proportion find the Navy an attractive career, and retention of experienced ratings is becoming perhaps an even bigger problem than recruitment.

Pay is outside the scope of this book but it is worth noting that making life on board attractive is expensive and pay increases, perhaps only while living on ships (Hard Lying money) might be a cheaper solution. The design of ships to function with smaller crews seems essential, though this may be counterproductive if it means that the small crew has to work unreasonably hard. High utilisation of ships with long periods at sea is also unpopular, while the old attraction of a sailor's life, travel, means much less given the modern availability of cheap foreign holidays.

It may also be necessary to consider manning arrangements which permit personnel to take one voyage off in every three as in merchant ships. The alternative, double crews as in missile submarines, may be easier to organise. It was intended to operate the hydrofoil *Speedy* with two crews on 8-hour shifts, though she was disposed of before this system could be tried.

The Royal Navy has accepted the principle of women working at sea in operational warships but the response from WRNS already in the Service has not been great.

Provision of living space on a warship is always bound to be expensive and on cost grounds alone there is a good case for smaller crews. As is often the way, it is likely that all the measures discussed above will have to be used to some extent: higher pay, small-

[5] 'Maintaining the Fleet', *Maritime Defence* (May, 1990) based on a National Audit Office report.

er crews, better accommodation standards and more time ashore.

The existing Navy The Navy as it exists now is a constraint in many ways. Officers and men are trained to fight with existing types of ships and to use existing equipment. Any radical changes would necessitate considerable retraining not simply in the actual operation of new styles of ship or equipment but also in their strategic and tactical employment.

It would not be easy to operate novel vessels in company with existing ones. For example, a SWATH, with far better seakeeping than conventional ships, would lose much of its advantage if it had to operate in company with them; similarly an MCM hovercraft cruising at about 65 knots would not fit well in a squadron whose other ships cruised at 14 knots. Even lesser changes, such as a shift from gas turbines to diesel electric machinery, bring problems in training and logistics.

Major changes can only come slowly, as budget restrictions alone will ensure, but the prolonged transitional period can be difficult. On the other hand, the world is changing rapidly and the fact that changes in the Navy must be slow only strengthens the case for starting now. It is not unfair to suggest that the Royal Navy, like all disciplined services, is by nature conservative, and its reluctance to innovate is greatest when funds are scarce.

Commitments The freedom with which ships and funds can be deployed is constrained by Britain's commitments to friends and allies. For example, protection of the Falkland Islands still ties up a number of surface ships and the occasional submarine, and the Antarctic Dependencies require the retention of the patrol ship *Endeavour*.[6]

NATO is the biggest such commitment: in the 1950s the Royal Navy was committed to provide seventy frigates or destroyers, and more recently the figure has been 'about fifty'. In July 1990, this was reduced to forty even though there has been no reduction in the capability of the Soviet Navy.

There are other commitments, by both treaty and moral obligation, which could lead to conflict. At the time of writing, the United Nations has imposed sanctions on Iraq as a result of her invasion of

---

[6] *Endeavour* is now, however, under renewed threat from defence cuts.

Kuwait, an operation which will surely require a multinational naval force. There are also commitments as noted above to Hong Kong, to other small nations of the Commonwealth such as the Seychelles, to friendly states in the Middle East, and to Australia and New Zealand.

Sea conditions The sea itself imposes major constraints on naval policy and the design of warships. It is big, cold, wet, rough (sometimes very rough), corrosive and hard when it hits you. All these aspects have to be taken into account.

The Atlantic is a big ocean:

Atlantic distances

New York - Southampton	3188 nautical miles
Halifax - Liverpool	2000
Panama - Southampton	4569
Rotterdam - Narvik	1137

The potential battleground is some 3000 miles from east to west and more than 1200 miles from north to south. Putting it another way, a 20-knot convoy will take at least six days to cross, and the escorts, which have to search and hunt and may zig-zag, will travel a much greater distance at a higher speed. Long endurance, or at least the capability for rapid refuelling, is essential.

The sea is rarely calm, and often rough, but 'roughness' is not easy to describe numerically.[7] Waves are generated by wind blowing over the surface for a considerable time and distance but, since ocean waves travel for thousands of miles, there can be no simple relationship between local wind speed and wave height. A reasonable indication for well developed waves is given in Table 7.

The figures given in Table 7 for probability of occurrence are averaged over the whole of the North Atlantic, for the whole year. Figure 3/1 compares this average probability with that for weather station India (off Northwest Scotland) both for the whole year and for the winter months only. The effect of rough weather on both men and machines is discussed in the next chapter, but it must be

---

[7] Adrian R J M Lloyd, *Seakeeping* (Chichester, 1989). This publication is for mathematicians only!

HMCS *Margaree* in heavy seas – 'cold, wet and hard'.

BLE 7: RELATIONSHIP BETWEEN WIND SPEED AND THE SIZE OF
WAVES IN THE NORTH ATLANTIC

e*	*Significant wave height (metres)*		*Sustained wind speed (knots)*		*Probability of sea state (percent)*	*Wave period (secs)*		*Likely wave length (metres, approximate)*
	range	*mean*	*range*	*mean*		*range*	*most probable*	
	0.0-0.1	0.05	0-6	3.0	0.7	–	–	–
	0.1-0.5	0.3	7-10	8.5	6.8	3.3-12.8	7.5	90
	0.5-1.25	0.88	11-16	13.5	23.7	5.0-14.8	7.5	90
	1.25-2.5	1.88	17-21	19.0	27.8	6.1-15.2	8.8	123
	2.5-4.0	3.25	22-27	24.5	20.6	8.3-15.5	9.7	148
	4.0-6.0	5.0	28-47	37.5	13.2	9.8-16.2	12.4	238
	6.0-9.0	7.5	48-55	51.5	6.1	11.8-18.5	15.0	350
	9.0-14.0	11.5	56-63	59.5	1.1	14.2-18.6	16.4	424
	14.0	14.0	63	63.0	0.05	18.0-23.7	20.0	615

ote that Sea State numbers are not Beaufort numbers (which refer to wind speed).

clear that the ability of a ship to fight effectively in northern latitudes is severely limited in the winter months. Effectiveness will of
course be greater in the southerly latitudes of the Azores.

It is widely believed, incorrectly, that waters close to the land are
sheltered and so are safer, but even in the English Channel high
winds and seas are not uncommon. The 50-year wave height is 20
metres almost to the Isle of Wight, with a corresponding wind
speed of 30m/s. Many inshore disasters have shown the danger of
underestimating coastal seas, such as the breaking in half of the
French torpedo boat *Branlebas* off Dartmouth in World War II.

The impact of steep, high waves can damage the structure of the
ship. Above the still waterline, the impact of the sea on bridge
fronts, weapon mountings, windows and, particularly, bow doors,

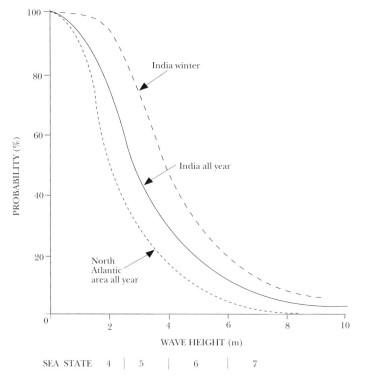

Figure 3/1: Percentage probability of waves exceeding a given height, in
    (a) North Atlantic, all year; (b) Weather station India, all year; and (c) Weather
    station India, winter months only.

can cause damage, often followed by flooding.

When the bows lift out of the water in pitching and then slam down there is a severe local pressure which can damage plating and sonar domes. The force due to these pressures over the fore end adds to the overall wave bending stresses and will both increase the maximum stress and increase its extent forward of amidships. Each time the ship slams, the fatigue life of the ship will be reduced. Eventually, cracks will appear at sharp corners, the ends of super-structure blocks and wherever the structure has discontinuities. If the general stress is high or if unsuitable steel has been used, such cracks can spread across the upper deck and even down the sides. The stress due to bad weather and especially high speed in bad weather sets a term to the life of any warship.

The temperature of salt water cannot fall below 4°C, but the Arctic air temperature can be much lower. The effect of cold air on men is made worse by the chill factor due to wind speed. At the end of World War II a distinction was drawn between Arcticisation and Winterisation. The former then seemed very expensive, involving heaters round all exposed moving equipment, stiffening at the waterline to resist thin ice, and much else. Winterisation was much less demanding, and since there seemed no pressing need for the Royal Navy to operate in the Arctic, the cheaper solution was chosen.

Changes in the political and strategic balance have increased the likelihood of British and other NATO ships operating in freezing conditions. For example, support to northern Norway has increased in importance, as have under-ice operations by sub-marines. On the other hand, warships now carry less upper deck equipment, insulation has improved as has air conditioning, and the cost of full Arcticisation is hence relatively less, though still appreciable. Suitable steels must be used as many mild steels become brittle at low temperatures when exposed to explosive loading or collision.

Salt water is corrosive. Upper deck fittings and weapons are exposed to salt spray and the preservation and cure of rusting is a labour intensive and boring task. All too often the problem is exacerbated by poor design, with water traps and with dissimilar metals in contact. It is often forgotten that stainless steel corrodes quickly in salt water (though every housewife knows not to put her stainless steel knives into salt water). Design to avoid rust traps, sensible choice of materials, cathodic protection and good paints, properly applied, can do much to keep corrosion at bay but it remains a threat to the life of a steel ship.

The sea also imposes certain technological constraints on the equipment of warships, with consequent implications for naval policy. Electro-magnetic radiation does not travel far through sea water. Detection of a submerged submarine by eye is unlikely below periscope depth, and then only in good conditions, and radio communication with submerged submarines is possible only using buoys or at very low frequencies.

For this reason, sound remains the principal means of detecting submerged submarines. For many years, Soviet submarines were very much more noisy than those of major NATO navies, which meant that they could be heard at long range by fixed installations on the sea bed (SOSUS), by towed arrays and even by hull-mounted sonars. Later Soviet submarines are much quieter, lessening, though not eliminating, the value of passive sonars. The transmission of sound through water is, however, very complicated and is outside the scope of this book.[8]

Active sonars are normally limited to much shorter ranges, while longer ranges are generally obtained only at low frequencies. Low-frequency sonars are inherently large and their use discloses the position of the user. Even the best future active sonars will have shorter range than that achieved by today's passive sets against older Soviet submarines, and hence more sonars and thus more ships are needed.

Perhaps the final thought on the sea is that it is best suited to carry heavy loads at fairly low speed. Attempts to go faster are bound to be expensive and may be dangerous.

---

[8] For a good introduction, see Norman Friedman, *World Naval Weapon Systems* (Annapolis, 1989).

4

Design Philosophy

We apprehend that it is the object of our labours, as it is of science, to endeavour to produce the best effects with given means.

THE CHATHAM COMMITTEE OF NAVAL ARCHITECTS, 1842

The effective and economic use of resources is fundamental to design philosophy, but it also includes layout, aesthetics and such considerations as ship life. The more detailed aspects of ship design are considered in the next chapter. Naval officers, historians and naval architects are all sure that some designs are 'better' than others, and there is usually a fair measure of agreement on which ships are the good ones. Almost inevitably, such judgements are historical, made retrospectively at the end of, or after, the long life of a ship; as such, these judgements may be unduly influenced by performance at the end of that life, when the ship may well have been used for tasks very different from those for which it was designed.

A good design will be right in most aspects, which pre-supposes that the Staff Requirement was a sound forecast of the basic performance and capability needed over 20-30 years. Basic requirements are for good sea boats, conveniently laid out to function in peace and war, with reliable and easily maintained equipment and with adequate margins for essential additions.

Above all, with a few important exceptions, the ships which are generally regarded as good designs are versatile as built and adaptable to the new tasks which occur during their lives. The exceptions are specialised ships with a single clear role which persists throughout their lives and which are well fitted and armed for that role. The World War II Loch class is probably one of the best designs of the century; in their specialised ASW role these ships had the most advanced sensors and weapons in the world, fitted in an easily-built hull of adequate performance. With minor changes, they were effective for at least a decade after the war. The Ton class MCMVs were another successful specialist design, though in their case equipment and even machinery has changed considerably during their working lives; they were versatile and adaptable within a limited area.

The post war *Blackwood*s were probably over-specialised in ASW for peacetime operation; a medium calibre gun would have made them more versatile at little extra cost. Adaptable usually means spacious, and most aircraft carriers have proved quite adaptable to new types of aircraft, and even to new command systems, since their spacious hangars and workshops are fairly easy to modify. It may be that the greatest failing of the Royal Navy's armoured hangar carriers was that the cramped hangar was difficult and expensive to adapt for new aircraft – consider for example, the protracted modernisation of *Victorious*.[1]

It is even more difficult to set out the desirable qualities of a good fleet, considered in more depth in Chapter 8. Inevitably, debate centres on quality versus quantity within a limited budget.

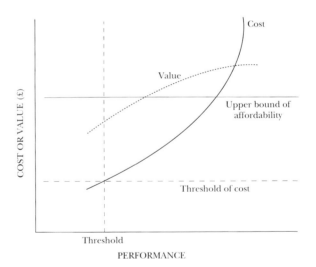

Figure 4/1: Cost and value of performance.

[1] David K Brown, *A Century of Naval Construction* (London, 1983).

Operation modelling of specific encounters will usually show that big ships are the most cost-effective, a phenomenon which Khudyakov[2] refers to as the 'super battleship paradox'.

Figure 4/1 illustrates the relationship between cost, performance and value for individual ships, though it is doubtful if such a relationship can actually be quantified for a real ship. In general, as performance is increased, cost rises exponentially, while capability, the value of the system, levels off. There is a lower threshold below which performance is inadequate to carry out the tasks of a warship and it must be assumed that the value is greater than the cost at that point. There is also an upper boundary of affordability set by the need for numbers and by political will. The band between these upper and lower bounds is usually small and diminishing and, if it gets too small for a given category, that type of ship will disappear from the Navy, as did the fleet carrier.[3]

The debate between quality and quantity can never be resolved, and the balance struck will change with time. For example, the quieter Soviet submarines lead to the requirement for much higher performance from their hunters, while reduced detection ranges demand an increase in the number of ships. On the other hand, the reduced threat from the Soviet Union suggests a slight shift towards quantity, as does the increasing threat in other parts of the world.

Ship life and replacement policy

It is difficult to specify precisely the point at which the long life of a warship actually starts. The process of design usually begins with a number of wide-ranging policy papers and design studies; for example, the very lengthy 'Future Light Frigate' studies were developed, after further variation as the Types 24 and 25, into the Type 23, Duke class. The Staff Target (Sea) can be taken as the formal moment of conception though serious design is likely to have been in hand for at least a year.

Table 8 shows a typical class history for postwar British frigates and will be used as a basis for discussing alternatives.

---

[2] L Y Khudyakov, *Analytical Design of Ships* (Leningrad, 1980).
[3] David K Brown and Eric C Tupper, *The Naval Architecture of Surface Warships*, Transactions RINA (London, 1988).

The Type 25, an attempt at a cheap frigate. Much of the thinking went into the Type 23.

There can be few who would suggest that there should be no change to the military capability of ships over a period of thirty-four years, particularly when it is appreciated that some equipment will already have been in service for some time when the Staff Target was agreed.

There is much less agreement on how to resolve the problem of ageing in the ship and its equipment. The traditional answer was mid-life modernisation, in which a ship was gutted after some ten years in service and given a new weapon fit, sometimes virtually changing in role as a result. Some modernisations were seen as very valuable, such as the conversion of the destroyers of the Emergency

TABLE 8: TYPICAL RECENT FRIGATE CLASS HISTORY

	Years
Staff Target to completion of first ship	8
Continue building similar ships	6
Ship life in service	20 +
TOTAL	34

War Programme to Type 15 and 16 AS frigates, which had a long and effective life afterwards. Others, such as the *Leander* modernisations, though still effective, were, at £70 million, almost as costly as a new ship.

It is extremely difficult to compare the true cost of modernisation with that of new building, due to the different overheads involved and the different way in which costs are brought to account, but there can be no doubt that it is expensive to strip out a warship and rebuild it. In particular, the installation of the new equipment has to be carried out through doors and hatches with a few shipping openings rather than by the much cheaper method of module construction.

A modular design of ship, in which large boxes of systems are installed complete (see page 109) may ease the problem of modernisation, but only if the new equipment is broadly similar in geometry and in its demands on services to the older unit. It is hard to see that any modular system would have helped to replace Sea Slug with horizontal hangar stowage by Sea Dart with missiles stowed vertically in a drum. The more limited improvements, referred to by the Royal Navy as 'capability update' would almost certainly be eased by modular design, and in this aspect the simple and more flexible 'cellularity' has probably most to offer. The ability to extend weapon compartments into soft areas is most valuable.

It is also worth thinking about the timing of any update. Halfway through the service life is up to twenty-four years from the Staff Target, and there may well be advantages in bringing the update well forward. Changes made during building are disruptive and hence expensive and it may be sensible to defer most changes to an update a few years after acceptance. The RN escort carriers (CVEs) built at Seattle in World War II were delivered without any of the changes seen as essential by their operators and they were taken directly to Vancouver for a well-planned 6-week update before entering service.[4]

A more radical solution which is often proposed is the short-life ship, thrown away after about ten years. The implication is that the extension of the life of the ship from ten to twenty years adds greatly to first cost by demands for expensive corrosion protection and

---

[4] David K Brown, 'The Development of the British Escort Carrier' *Warship* (London, 1983).

long-life equipment. This is probably not true; with modern coatings and materials, mere life extension is not expensive. A more convincing argument is the cost of updating capability. The real objection to the short-life ship is political; such a ship will still look impressive at ten years, when the last ships of the class have only just completed, and the temptation to run it on rather than replace it has always proved overwhelming in the past.

A much more attractive approach is to design for about twenty years and sell to the Third World at about nine years, while the ship is in good condition and fairly up to date, ordering a replacement for the Royal Navy. An economic price would be about half the UPC, and at this level both sides would feel that they had achieved a good bargain. Since export sales of new frigates are now uncommon, such a second-hand business would increase the amount of work in British shipyards and suppliers while reducing the average age of the fleet,[5] though other major navies might adopt the same strategy, thus depressing the market and leaving the Royal Navy with a proportion of ageing ships.

There is no single answer to the problems of ship obsolescence and replacement, as policy on this issue is influenced by the severity of the perceived threat and by the economy of the country. A compromise using some features of several of the alternatives outlined above seems possible. Ships could be designed for a 20-year life, with generous margins to permit some enhancement, and in such a way as to reduce the effort needed (for instance, by using cellularity). Any opportunity to sell early and replace should be encouraged and government financial procedures should be developed to simplify such sales.

Standards

The British Naval Engineering Standards (NES) and the equivalent USN MILSPECs are often derided as 'gold plating'. This is far from the truth; they represent the codified historical experience of the Navy, they have been derived from hard and often painful experience and modified in the light of new technology and changes in the availability of materials. Nevertheless, with about 500 such stan-

---

[5] Sami Faltas, *Warships and the World Market* (Amsterdam, 1985).

dards in operation it is inevitable at any one time that some will be obsolescent.

> Such standards must change from time to time and it is as proper for the designer to challenge them as it is foolish for him to ignore the accumulated wisdom contained in them.[6]

It should never be forgotten that a warship is the biggest and most complicated single artifact in the Defence Budget and the only one for which there is no prototype. Many prototype aircraft and tanks are built and, after an arduous programme of trials, one or more can be fired on with live ammunition. One complete airframe is tested to destruction under fatigue loading.

The first of a new class of warship will be given lengthy trials, at the end of which only minor rectification will be undertaken before she becomes an operational unit of the fleet. If a serious design problem should emerge, it will affect up to six more ships in various stages of construction. It is only possible to take the risk of committing several hundreds of millions of pounds to an untested ship design because the materials, components and procedures have been proven and tested and the results formalised in standards.

Some years ago, the Royal Navy went even further and specified a limited range of standard equipment (pumps, fans and fin stabilisers, to name but a few), allowing identical components to be used in several classes over a long period of time. This procedure had several advantages, such as reduced spares holding, simplified training and purchase at bulk rates, but there were the corresponding disadvantages of creeping obsolescence and very limited scope for competitive purchasing. The opposite approach, the free market, also has its problems, in that the cheapest item of equipment is also very likely to be the biggest and heaviest, thus increasing the size of the ship. Spares holdings are also larger and may prove difficult at the end of a long ship life. Reliability can only be assured by exhaustive testing which, to be fair, must be carried out on samples from all potential suppliers in a free market. Design is always a compromise, however, and rigid policies should be avoided.

---

[6] David K Brown, 'Defining a Warship' *Naval Engineers' Journal* ASNE (Washington, March 1986). I am very proud that this quotation is framed on the wall of NAVSEA, Washington.

There seems to be a basic difference in design philosophy between the Soviet Union and the NATO powers. The latter seek to introduce new technology as soon as possible in Mk II or III equipment, while Soviet designers prefer to refine old technology, then eventually make a two-generation leap. The standard example was the Soviet Union's highly-evolved thermionic valve technology, developed while the West adopted transistors, followed by a jump to the second-generation computer chip.[7]

Corrosion protection is a favourite area for critics and, at a total of 2 percent of the total cost of a frigate, some examination is justified. The value of both cathodic protection and good paints in extending the interval between refits and reducing the repair work required is hard to quantify but is clearly far in excess of the saving possible by adopting a cheaper scheme; no-one would suggest an unpainted ship. A proper conservatism in the use of well proven paints and protection systems must be combined with a readiness to try new products.

Architecture

The architectural arrangement of a ship, its layout, greatly affects its cost, capability and the convenience with which the crew carry out their tasks, but architecture is difficult to set out in guidelines and impossible to specify in a contract.

> A modern warship is an assembly of spaces, many of which serve more than one function, interacting in a complex manner and located within an envelope whose proportions and shape are set by hydrodynamic and other considerations. Furthermore, the structure is supported on, and loaded by, the sea in a most irregular fashion whilst the arrangement of partitions is governed by structural continuity and the containment of damage to a far greater extent than in buildings on shore.[8]

Space is a word frequently used, often without sufficient care in defining what is meant. In a warship space may be a volume, as in

---

[7] Jim W Kehoe, Ken S Brower and Herb A Meier 'US and Soviet Ship Design Practices, 1950-1980' *Proceedings USNI* (Annapolis, 1982).
[8] David K Brown, *The Architecture of Frigates*, RINA Symposium on Anti Submarine Warfare (London, 1987).

fuel tanks, or a deck area, as in bunk spaces, or even a length, as in upper deck arrangement. Its position, both absolute and relative to other spaces, is always important, while its shape, too, can matter. In a typical frigate there are some 400 compartments and an infinity of ways in which they can be arranged, and space is expensive; as a rule of thumb, it costs £5,000 to enlarge a frigate by one square metre of empty space.

The approach to layout is best addressed sequentially, bearing in mind that each major decision pre-empts a large number of lesser options. It is often necessary to return to an earlier stage and challenge the decisions made.

The objective of the naval architect is never clearcut, and warships incorporate several inherent contradictions. Though a warship is designed to fight, it will spend most of its life at peace and will be in harbour more than it is at sea.

Fighting is the true purpose of a warship and must be given priority, but the convenience of the crew should be seen as only slightly less important in the light of difficulties in recruiting and retention.

Layout will probably begin with the upper deck arrangement, as

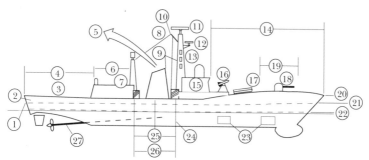

1 Freeboard limit	12 Navigation radar	22 3 Deck
2 Towed sonar	13 Communications and electronic	23 Critical dimensions of
3 Landing spot as near amidships	warfare antennae	magazine
as possible	14 Separation to reduce motions at	24 Alignment of bulkheads
4 Helicopter deck	bridge	and superstructure
5 Hot gas plume	15 Length of waveguide	25 Two machinery units
6 Hangar	16 Surface to air missile	(separated?)
7 Close in weapon system	17 Surface to surface missile	26 Uptakes and downtakes
8 Roof aerial	18 Green sea loading	(linking upper deck and
9 Electronic clearance	19 Physical arc of training	hold layout)
10 Excited mast (height specified)	20 1 Deck	27 Shaft rake (height of
11 Surveillance radar	21 2 Deck	machinery)

Figure 4/2: An indication of the critical dimensions, including physical and electronic clearances, which set the upper deck length of a frigate.

weapon and sensor arcs of fire and clearances usually set the length and size of the ship. Figure 4/2 shows some of the critical dimensions affecting the deck layout of a traditional frigate. The uptakes firmly key together the machinery and deck arrangement.

Upper deck arrangement is simpler if the superstructure is kept to a minimum, and this is also desirable since reduction of windage and topweight help stability. A spacious upper deck can accept new equipment or deckhouses to accommodate spaces displaced from soft areas below. The minimum superstructure will be quite large if it has to accommodate a big helicopter hangar, but beyond that the essential spaces are a very small bridge, a chart house, access lobbies and upper deck storage. Some ESM offices may also be needed high up to keep down the length of wave guides.

Vulnerability considerations (see page 73) will have a major impact on layout through zoning policy and the separation of key spaces, such as machinery. Inside the ship, a key decision is that of access routes and the run of main passages. Access routes account for some 15 percent of the space in a frigate, rising to 20 percent on the critical 2 deck, the prime piece of real estate. The need for passages must be reduced as much as possible by siting compartments so that traffic is reduced, but provision for routes found essential should be generous.

Since the passages are the usual routes for services such as power and water, they must be routed to ensure the survival of at least one leg of duplicated runs. Sided passages provide maximum separation at the expense of maximum exposure to damage, while the cost in space compared with a single centreline passage is considerable. The arrangement of passages is likely to determine the position of hatches, which should lie within the line of uptakes so that there is as much continuous deck structure to take the load as possible.

Simple modelling of storing routes, including those for replenishment at sea, and a good deal of thought, should lead to a layout which, though a compromise, will be effective in war and convenient in peace.

A warship is the representative of her country, a projection of power, and should look the part; a national style is desirable. Quite small changes in the position, shape and slope of the upper works can have a major impact on appearance. A good-looking ship is the outcome of caring design; she must look good for twenty to thirty years, so extremes of fashion should be avoided. Sir Hugh Casson's timeless style for the *Britannia* is a good example.

'Unstable' designs

All designs tend to grow in size due to the pressure to incorporate new weapons and systems as a counter to an ever growing threat; only a much weaker force operates in the other direction, acting to reduce unit cost in the hope of increasing numbers. There are certain size and cost brackets in which one force, usually growth, is almost irresistible.

The original concept for the Duke class (Type 23 frigate) was for a small ship which could tow a sonar array and provide a landing deck for a helicopter, but with no hangar and virtually no armament, costing some £65 million.[9] The ship envisaged was too expensive to be expendable, and yet was unable to defend itself. The whole concept was therefore philosophically 'unstable', and had to shrink to a cost level at which its loss could be accepted, or grow to a cost of over £100 million in order to allow for some defensive armament.

It is interesting to speculate on what is an 'acceptable' loss. In Nelson's day, the Third Rate of 74 guns was often used in risky operations, while in both World Wars the destroyer was the expendable ship. Such ships cost about 0.3 to 0.5 percent of the Naval budget, which today would correspond to £12.5 million. Perhaps we are more profligate today or have less choice; today the figure of £35-40 million seems to be thought of as an acceptable loss. However, human life is valued more highly today than in the past, and even expendable ships must have small crews and ample life-saving equipment.

The cheap helicopter carrier lies in another unstable zone, as discussed in Chapter 9 below. Its value lies mainly in its payload and the importance of its aircraft to the success of an operation. It is all too easy to justify increases in active and passive equipment to defend such a valuable asset, until such increases escalate to a cost which cannot be borne.

The cheap corvette, and even cheap helicopter carriers, are pos-

---

[9] Sir Lindsay Bryson, *The Procurement of a Warship* Transactions RINA (London, 1984).

sible, but very firm control at the top is needed to ensure that the requirements do not drive the cost to a level which cannot be afforded.

Vulnerability

Even in peacetime, warships are at greater risk than are merchant ships; exercises at close quarters, without lights or radar, can lead to collisions, and the extensive fuel, hydraulic and electrical systems can start a fire. Accidents to RN ships from 1945 to 1984[10] have included 27 explosions, 71 major fires (some figures suggest as many as ten per year), 115 collisions (plus ten during the 'Cod Wars') and 50 groundings. Included in these figures are the losses of four submarines, two frigates and four minesweepers, together with several other ships whose damage was so severe that they were not repaired (including an aircraft carrier).

The normal 'seamanlike precautions' required against these hazards form the lower boundary of damage protection. In particular, there is about a one in four chance of a collision damaging a bulkhead, thus flooding two compartments. The Institution of Naval Architects said of merchant ships in 1867 that no ship is well designed which will not float with two compartments flooded, yet today passenger ships do not always meet this standard and most cargo ships will sink if one compartment is open to the sea. A frigate should float with any three main compartments flooded and usually with four.

Vulnerability in its true, warship sense (that is, vulnerability to the effects of enemy weapons) can best be understood in the context of more specific, technical aspects of warship design. These are considered in the next chapter.

---

[10] G H Ransome, 'Accidents and Losses since 1945' *Warship Supplement* (World Ship Society, Kendal, 1987-8).

5

Technical Features of Warship Design

Ships are built to fight, and must be able to take blows as well as to inflict them.

ADMIRAL OF THE FLEET LORD CHATFIELD

The design of warships is, or should be, dominated by the need for resistance to enemy attack. Damage to ships in peacetime is happily rare; in war it is almost certain.

TABLE 9: FREQUENCY OF DAMAGE TO RN DESTROYERS IN WORLD WAR II[1]						
Year	1939-40	40-41	41-42	42-43	43-44	44-45
No in commission	135	154	170	185	197	147
No damaged or sunk	124	108	106	60	79	20

In the desperate early years of World War II damage was virtually certain in each period of 12 months, and these are global figures; in many specific campaigns the risks were given even higher. In the Falklands, too, sixteen of the twenty-three destroyers and frigates were hit.[2]

Warship design must take into account the possibility of damage from a wide variety of anti-ship weapons, as shown in Figure 5/1.

The effects of this bewildering array of weapons can be grouped as shown in Table 10.

Such a table can only be a generalisation; fires have occasionally

---

[1] David K Brown, *The Battleworthy Frigate* Transactions North East Coast Institution of Engineers and Shipbuilders (Newcastle 1990).
[2] J D Brown, *The Royal Navy and the Falklands War* (London, 1987).

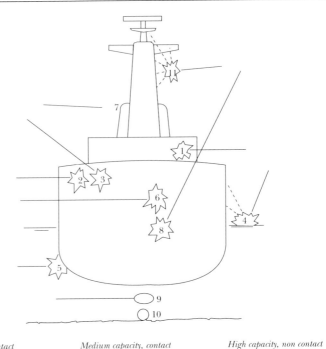

Low capacity, contact
1 cannon shell, HE and AP

High capacity, contact
2 HE shell
3 HE bomb
4 HE bomb, near miss
5 contact torpedo or mine

Medium capacity, contact
6 missile, sea skimming and
   SAP shell
7 missile, high level
8 medium case bomb

High capacity, non contact
9 magnetic-fused torpedo
10 ground mine
11 proximity-fused missile

Figure 5/1: The Constructor's Nightmare: a diagrammatic view of some of the conventional weapons which may be used against a warship.

TABLE 10: EFFECTS OF CONVENTIONAL ANTI-SHIP WEAPONS

	Missiles	Bombs	Shells	Torpedoes	Mines	Splinters and small arms
Fire	☆	☆	☆			
Flood				☆	☆	
Structural Collapse	☆	☆		☆	☆	
Shock				☆	☆	
Blast	☆	☆				
Impact	☆	☆	☆			☆

been started by underwater explosions, for example. The nature of the fuse (contact, proximity or delay) also affects the type and extent of damage.

Objective

The common philosophy of the US Navy and the Royal Navy is well illustrated by their respective slogans 'Fight Hurt' and 'To Float, to Move, to Fight'. The problems involved have no easy solutions.

Some modern weapons are so powerful that one hit will disable a frigate. This encourages the philosophy that all resources should be put into preventing a hit and none into limiting the effects when a hit is scored. This is mistaken; no protective screen is totally effective all the time, so some weapons will get through. If the ship is totally lacking in resistance to damage the enemy's task is greatly eased; as always in design, compromise is necessary.

It is less easy to say what additional precautions are worthwhile, but the picture may be clearer from the enemy's point of view. Lethal missiles and torpedoes are surprisingly few in number and very expensive. Since they are not 100 percent reliable it would be normal to fire at least two against an unprotected target. If defensive measures compel the use of three or four weapons to ensure a kill, the effectiveness of the fleet is correspondingly reduced.

This approach gives the first guideline, that the enemy's task must be made difficult; warships should not be put out of action, or even sunk, by a trivial hit. The designer's success in achieving the right balance can only be judged with hindsight, after battle, by Naval Boards of Enquiry and Parliamentary Committees. After the Falklands war the latter found that 'Fire precautions and damage control are not appropriate matters on which to cut corners; the resulting economies are false if they contribute to loss of lives or ships.'[3]

In accepting the Committee's view, the Ministry, rightly, pointed out that some compromise was always essential. Naval Boards of Enquiry took a somewhat similar line and, though recommending many detailed changes, thought the balance of defence about

---

[3] *Material Lessons of the Falklands War* House of Commons Defence Committee Report (London, 1983).

right. Such conclusions need to be balanced against the circumstances of that war; no RN ship was hit by an underwater weapon. Only five missiles were used and most of the damage was due to World War II-style iron bombs. Against modern weapons the task force might have suffered more heavily.

Design teams in all countries have been alerted by recent damage to frigates in the Gulf. Though weapons are improving, there are also some developments which aid defence. In the following sections the design problems can be set out fairly fully, but the possible solutions which are being worked on can be given only in general terms. There are major organisational problems in any such design development, in that limitation of damage (the aim under discussion here) affects every technical department, the way in which a ship is operated and the training of sailors. The United Kingdom set up a special organisation a few years to bring together all aspects, and this seems to be running well and to have the necessary authority.

There is little prospect of using armour to keep enemy weapons out of a ship of frigate size. Even an Exocet, a small weapon, has the mass and almost the velocity of a World War I 13.5in SAP shell. It might penetrate some 30cm of armour (the thickness of *Iowa*'s belt) though a thinner plate would render it unfit to detonate. Even a 30mm armour-piercing shell will penetrate 15cm of steel. On the other hand, much of the damage to ships and their equipment from high explosive warheads is from quite small splinters, which can be stopped by a few centimetres of plate, reducing the amount of damage by about 99 percent. Light protection to exposed wave guides, cable runs and electronic spaces is valuable and, if combined with the structure, need not be expensive.

Layout

The most effective protective measure is intelligent layout, and the guiding principle here is 'concentrate, duplicate, separate'. In older ships the vital components of a weapon system were often distributed over the length of the ship and the loss of any of these components or the links between them would put the whole system out of action. The first basic principle is to *concentrate* all vital components, including the power supply, in one area of the ship. This is not quite as easy as it sounds, as major design components such as the main radar and the AIO are common to most weapon systems. However, concentration is the first aim.

Where possible, vital systems should then be *duplicated,* and the alternative systems widely *separated.* Modern micro electronics and electric propulsion enable the full philosophy to be applied to smaller ships than in the past; the advanced frigate (see Chapter 7) is virtually double ended (that is, it retains some capability with major damage at one end) at about 4500 tons, though some of the alternative systems are of lower capability.

The clearest example of this philosophy is the unit system of machinery, introduced in World War I. In simple form, this meant that a warship would have four machinery spaces arranged alternatively (boiler room, engineroom, boiler room, engineroom), on the assumption that a hit affecting two spaces would leave at least one engine and one boiler room working. The unit system was used by most navies in cruisers and above, but the US Navy applied it in World War II destroyers. The unit system proved an effective measure in preserving mobility after hit from both above and underwater weapons. A recent computer study showed the following chances of a ship remaining mobile after a single hit: one unit, two spaces (for example boiler room, engineroom) – 50 percent; two units, adjacent – 75 percent; and two units, separated – 90 percent.

The same approach can be applied to accommodation, with the crew, of all ranks, living close to their action stations, complete with cooking, toilet and other facilities. An arrangement of this sort much reduces the time that hatches and doors are open while the crew moves from cruising to action stations. On the other hand, such a layout is very inconvenient for peacetime living. A reasonable compromise is to split accommodation into two blocks, forward and aft, and then to divide the ship into five zones, each with at least emergency cooking and sanitation.

Duplicating the AIO complex forward and aft seems,at first sight, very expensive. However, the cost of a command and control system lies mainly in development; duplicate hardware and software is not expensive, though there will be additional installation and setting-to-work costs.

There are many other layout problems, some of which have no clear answer, such as whether to site the operations room complex high up to reduce the length of wave guides and cables or low down as a protection from splinters. Fuel should always be kept low, partly for protection and partly so that it is easy to put a foam blanket over any burning fuel.

It is not easy to choose the best arrangements for service runs and main passages. If they are arranged down either side of the ship, the services are very vulnerable to splinters, though the alternative system on the undamaged side should survive. A missile with a delay fuse exploding in the middle of the ship will take out both runs however they are arranged, which shows the importance of concentrating all components and avoiding long cable runs.

The major direct cause of loss of British destroyers and frigates in World War II was structural failure, which accounting for an 41 percent of the losses. Of all destroyers hit by any weapon, 14 percent broke their backs. The modern torpedo or mine is designed to explode under the ship and break it apart. Although complete protection is not possible, there are a number of measures which can be taken to make the task of the weapon designer more difficult. Analysis of World War II loss and damage, and of the careful trials carried out against surplus hulls after the war, suggest that the following measures should be adopted:

□ Low stresses and good margin against buckling failure;

□ A deep hull so that only a part is destroyed by an explosion;

□ Avoidance of discontinuities, such as a short forecastle.

Thick protective plating may be used to contribute to girder strength. The non-contact, underwater explosion remains, however, the most serious threat to ships.

The Falklands showed that fire is a bigger hazard than it used to be and that serious fires usually involve fuel. Since that war many improvements in fire protection have been made, and more are under development. The essential steps are:

□ Limit the use of flammable materials and protect those which are essential (for example, fuel);

□ Confine the fire and smoke to a single compartment or zone. This implies isolating ventilation systems and ensuring that bulkheads are truly tight;

☐ Get the fire party to the fire quickly, with unobstructed passages and thermal imaging cameras to see through smoke and ensure good communications;

☐ Extinguish the fire. Automatic fire suppression systems such as that developed by Graviner to protect main battle tanks have shown the ability to put out major fires in dummy enginerooms in a small fraction of a second. Water fog is another very promising development;

☐ Finally, if the worst happens, it must be possible to evacuate the ship quickly; men will stay at their posts longer if they know they can get out. Sets of small personal breathing apparatus (ELSA) have been provided.

There can, it must be emphasised, be no invulnerable ship, and excessive attention to passive defence takes resources away from the primary role of the warship. Decision-making is already greatly aided by computer simulations of the effects of weapons on specific layouts. This is still a developing art and complete answers cannot always be obtained in time to affect the design. A particular problem is that past lessons show that survival of a ship may depend on quite minor details, and by the time these are identified and fed into the simulation, it is too late to change the design. Even now, however, it is often possible to see from such simulations that one proposed scheme is very much more effective than another, and this aids the designer in achieving a cost effective balance.

A new generation of warships can be much more battleworthy than ships now in service, and though such improvements are not free they need not be unduly expensive.

Machinery selection

The machinery of a warship must satisfy a number of differing requirements, summarised below, which conflict to some extent. The relative importance of these requirements varies with the primary role of the ship.

☐ An acceptable through-life cost, including development, procurement and running cost (with fuel);

☐ Reliability

☐ Vulnerability

☐ Noise reduction

☐ Compactness

Clearly, cost of procurement, including development, and the through-life cost of the operation will be important. Plumb[4] suggests that procurement costs form about 20 percent of the total life cost or 25 percent of the life cost discounted to Net Present Value (see Appendix 4) at 5 percent. Fuel economy is important, accounting for half of the through-life cost of the propulsion plant (40 percent discounted). The true cost of fuel, however, allowing for replenishment at sea, is very difficult to assess, as discussed below under endurance.

Reliability of the whole plant is probably over-riding. All components of modern machinery have a very high reliability, but failures nevertheless do occur. The total plant should be designed in such a way that any failure should have only a limited effect on the mobility of the ship and can quickly be made good. Vulnerability is closely linked to reliability, in that a single, enemy-induced 'failure' should have the least possible effect on mobility or other functions.

Noise reduction is important in all combat ships and vital in ASW vessels. Care is needed in considering the signature of the complete propulsion train, prime mover, transmission and shafting, and the propulsor. As usual, clear thought is needed to define which speeds and frequencies are important for each class.

The machinery plant should be compact, with as few critical dimensions as is possible. In particular, uptakes and downtakes should be of minimum size, with some flexibility in routing, as they have a critical impact on upper deck layout. Weight saving is less important than in the past.

There are many ways in which various prime movers and transmission systems may be combined. Prime movers include gas turbines, diesel engines and steam turbines, each of which has varia-

---

[4] Christopher M Plumb, *Warship Propulsion System Selection* (London, 1987).

tions in design and configuration. Transmission systems may involve gearing (which may be reversing), controllable pitch propellers or electric propulsion (with integrated or separate auxiliary load).

The gas turbine is the most frequent choice of prime mover for frigates of all navies. Marine gas turbines benefit from the tremendous investment in the development of aircraft engines and hence are very reliable and fairly economical. Little on-board maintenance is needed as the complete module is changed at intervals.

The most serious drawback with simple gas turbines is that specific fuel consumption rises rapidly at part load. The latest turbines are much better in this respect than earlier types, but to match diesels it is necessary to incorporate a more complex turbine cycle, which still requires expensive development work which would have to be paid for by the Navy. Gas turbine uptakes are very large and must have a straight run if excessive power losses are to be avoided. The exhaust gases are very hot and increase the infra red signature of the ship considerably. The US Navy has been developing the Racer plant, which is intended to recover some of this heat and use it to produce power; this will probably reduce infra red radiation at the same time.

Diesels, and in the case of warships this means medium speed engines, have a much flatter specific fuel consumption curve and, though the gap is narrowing, they have a smaller overall fuel consumption than gas turbines. Most diesels present problems in running at low power, (say below 30 percent of full speed rpm), at which level combustion problems can lead to the formation of carbon deposits. For this reason, a warship diesel plant nearly always consists of a number of individual units, of which only one or two will be used at low speed.

Diesels are heavier than gas turbines of the same power and this, together with their reciprocating action, makes it more difficult to isolate them from the sea and prevent excessive radiated noise. All such engines are multi-cylinder, with a very large number of moving parts. However, such parts are small and can be removed and replaced *in situ* without great difficulty, and reliability is good.

Steam plants went out of consideration by the Royal Navy in the 1960s due to the large number of men required for operation and maintenance, the wild heat produced and the length of time needed to start from cold. It seems likely that a modern plant could overcome these problems, but there is no European marine steam industry and development costs would be too high. In passing, it is interesting to note that old fashioned, slow speed, steam reciprocating engines driving paddle wheels were very quiet underwater, though extremely inefficient.

The most common arrangement of machinery in frigates is COGOG, usually with four gas turbines geared two to each of two shafts. Frequently, one pair of gas turbines is smaller than the other, working at near optimum specific fuel consumption for cruising speeds. The Rolls Royce SM1A – Spey – has a flatter fuel consumption curve than earlier engines and can be used in a COGAG arrangement with four identical engines, reducing spares holdings. CODOG is a similar, and frequently used, arrangement with diesels for cruising and gas turbines for full speed.

Gas turbines cannot have a reverse stage, as steam turbines do, because their very high rotational speed would cause serious loss of power from windage. Most gas turbine plants use controllable pitch propellers for reversing though, typically, these cause a loss of some 8 percent of efficiency due to poor blade sections near the roots together with the drag from larger shafts, shaft brackets and bosses. Controllable pitch propellers – at their design pitch – can usually be as quiet as fixed pitch propellers but are very noisy at other pitches (which might be set in error or occur due to wear in the mechanism). Many such installations require considerable maintenance. Attention has lately been given to reversing gearboxes, and these are now of the same order of cost as controllable pitch installations, and they are more efficient and reliable.

It was shown above that a ship's loss of mobility due to enemy action was less likely if machinery units were well separated; this is a concept most easily achieved in frigates using electric transmission. The Royal Navy introduced electric drive in the Type 23 for quietness at low speed when deploying a towed array and to overcome the low power problems of diesels. Electric drive also eliminates the reversing problem. The Type 23 installation has had few problems and an all-electric plant seems quite feasible. Care is needed to ensure that the low vulnerability of the distributed plant is not prejudiced by a common link, such as the single switchboard of World War I turbo-electric battleships of the US Navy.[5]

---

[5] Norman Friedman, *US Aircraft Carriers* (Annapolis, 1983).

For a current frigate design, full electric drive would have a higher first cost than COGOG with gearing. However, if even quieter ships are needed, electric drive should be cheaper than further refinement of geared drive. Due to the flexibility of a unitised plant, the electric prime movers can always operate close to peak efficiency, giving reductions in fuel cost. Further savings may come from reduced complement and equipment commonality through various classes.

It is clear that alternating current must be used and, with today's technology, the motors would be big. An 18MW motor might be 4.5 metres in diameter and 8.5 metres long. Developments in cooled rotors should, however reduce the size appreciably. Some considerable development is still required in the converters, also big and heavy, and in the switch gear.[6]

Even motors with cooled rotors will still be too big to use in the podded units often suggested. It seems likely that pods will only become practical when super cooled – cryogenic – motors become available. Podded propulsion should improve the waterflow into the propeller, increasing quiet speed and improving efficiency a little.

It is possible to use either gas turbines or diesels or a mix as the prime movers in an electric plant. If the engines are widely separated, there are problems in running the uptakes, particularly near the ends of the ship. The design studies considered later tend to show big prime movers in the motor rooms, with smaller units near the ends. There seem to be considerable advantages in using diesels at the ends, especially if underwater exhausts are used, but amidships either type of engine could be used. Even amidships, it is easier to run the uptakes for diesels, but gas turbines could be substituted if there were industrial or cost reasons for the choice.

Side exhausts, underwater, are shown for some designs in a later chapter. This is not accepted practice, but informed engineers see no great problem other than a small loss of efficiency. There would, however, be a considerable increase in underwater noise, and these units could not be used during low speed ASW operations. On the other hand, underwater exhausts would much reduce infra red signatures. In these studies the Type 23 practice is followed of putting

[6] P T Norton and M Murphy, *Realising the Potential – Full Electric Propulsion for Surface Warships* RINA Symposium 'The Future for Surface Warships' (London, 1990).

at least one diesel high in the ship with a long noise path to the water.

The United Kingdom now has a very small marine engineering industry with only one or two manufacturers of gas turbines, big diesels and gearboxes. A decision to buy from overseas or to change the type of prime mover or transmission might lead to the collapse of a major UK company, affecting maintenance of existing equipment. It is important and quite proper to consider the effect on industry of the choice of machinery.

Wind power has been considered for ASW ships because of its low propulsion noise. However, at the low speeds used in towed array work, most of the radiated noise comes from the auxiliary machinery, (the generators needed to power the sonar), and it does not seem that sails would help. In the Greenland area an efficient sail plan would, however, give about 12 knots for 80-90 percent of the year.

Endurance

In the early years of World War II, RN escorts were unable to accompany convoys across the Atlantic because they did not carry

A wind powered corvette. Such a vessel could make 12 knots for much of the time off Greenland, but the auxiliary machinery would still be noisy.

enough fuel. From 1942 onwards, the practice of replenishment at sea (RAS) was gradually adopted and later, more advanced RAS techniques, derived from USN methods, were introduced. RAS has been seen as a simple exercise in seamanship, and valuable in keeping task forces at sea.

Considerable efforts have been made to reduce the time a warship spends alongside an oiler during RAS but this is only the smaller part of the problem. The use of long-range passive sonars (towed arrays) means that the screening ships may be 100 miles from the centre of the task force or convoy – at least four hours steaming each away – and the true time for replenishment includes this transit time. The time a warship spends off station, travelling to the replenishment ship (AOR), refuelling and travelling back is many hours, and repeated every two to three days.

Modern AORs are expensive ships, vital to the success of today's operations, and hence they must be protected both by their own weapons and decoys – which increase their cost – and by a screen of escorts. Strict accounting would treat the cost of the AOR and its escorts as an overhead on the fuel costs of the fighting ships, more than doubling the shore bunker price of oil and hence making fuel economy measures even more attractive. Operationally, the need to escort the AOR reduces the number of escorts available for the primary task.

A possible alternative to RAS for frigates is the very long range (VLR) frigate which could operate for long periods without replenishment of any kind. Design studies are considered in later sections of this book for such ships with an endurance of thirty days at 18 knots, plus a 3000-mile margin. Thirty days is an arbitrary figure, corresponding to a voyage from New York to the United Kingdom and back at 10 knots mean speed. On the other hand, thirty days is a realistic operational figure, achieved at present using RAS methods and beyond which both crew and ship need a rest (relaxation for the former, maintenance for the latter).

The cost savings from VLR ships would be considerable; the number of AORs could be cut considerably (though there will older, short range ships for many years and the CVS will always need a supply of aviation fuel). More important, the task of the frigate force would be reduced and, even with a small cut in numbers offsetting the increased unit cost of the VLR ships, there would still be more frigates available for trade protection. In the fleet mix proposed later, these savings are traded for VLR ships and more helicopters.

Stealth

Surface ships can be detected by the signatures which they radiate, such as noise, infra-red and radar (either the beams from the sets which the ship is using or the reflected beam from a hostile radar). Such signatures may be used to classify the ship type, to provide the data needed to guide a homing weapon and to actuate the fuse when the weapon is sufficiently close. Unwanted radiation, particularly sound, can interfere with the performance of the ship's own sensors. All this provides full justification for the efforts made to reduce the radiated signatures of modern warships. It is not possible to make 4000 tonnes of steel invisible, but radiation can be reduced to levels at which it is easier to decoy or seduce the simple brain of an incoming missile. The principles of signature reduction are fairly simple and well known; the secret lies in the skill and experience with which these principles are applied.

Noise The underwater war is a silent war; the hunter must be quiet to hear his prey and if he should make a noise he himself may become the victim. Though there are a very large number of noise sources in a warship, their effects can be grouped into a fairly simple pattern.

At low speeds, below 12 to 15 knots,, the ship's signature is dominated by machinery noise. Out-of-balance forces, cylinder firing rates and other reciprocating forces all vibrate the machinery seats, and this is transmitted through the hull into the sea. Many of these noises give sharp peaks at particular frequencies and these peaks at discrete frequencies can also be used to identify the class, or even individual ships, and possibly to indicate the speed of the ship. Reducing machinery noise involves careful balancing, isolation of the machine from rigid pipe systems with flexible sections and, most important, supporting it on well damped, flexible mounts.

Passive measures such as these are now close to their developmental limit, and the next step may involve active noise cancellation. Active noise control involves sensing the disturbance – the noise – and using that information as the input to a control system which calculates the level of drive signals for actuators to generate the appropriate cancelling fields.[7]

Passive techniques require meticulous care in design and installation and rigorous inspection, since even a single rigid connection to the sea – a noise 'short' – can ruin the work. Noise radiation can be further reduced by surrounding the hull outside machinery spaces by a cloud of air bubbles emitted from a streamlined pipe surrounding the hull. This technique was tried by the Royal Navy on a patrol boat in 1917 and was not very successful because a suitable air compressor was not available. Development was stopped at the end of World War I in the mistaken belief that noise reduction was unnecessary in ships fitted with Asdic (active sonar). Attenuation can also be obtained by covering the hull with acoustic tiles.

Even at low speed, the propeller gives off a distinctive noise pattern. The water flow into the propeller is disturbed by the hull ahead of it and this irregular flow leads to fluctuations in the pressure on the blades. This noise is heard at a frequency of rotational speed times the number of blades, and can be used to determine the speed of the ship. This noise cannot be eliminated but may be reduced by reducing the irregularity of flow and then matching the number of blades and their skew to the flow.

A propeller works by generating a suction on the forward side (known to propeller designers as the back) and a pressure on the rear side (face). At higher speeds, the peak suction is enough to vaporise the water, a phenomenon known as cavitation. When these vapour bubbles collapse, particularly if they are in contact with the blade surface, they generate very intense, high frequency noise. Water also spills over the tip from pressure to suction side causing tip vortices similar to those seen at the wing tip of high flying aircraft. The centre of such vortices is a low pressure area and is usually where cavitation first starts.

The simple propellers of World War II escorts would cavitate at about 8 knots if in good condition and 5 to 6 knots if the edges were chipped, as they usually were. When the German acoustic homing torpedo was introduced, ships under attack would have to drop below this speed or use a noisy decoy. By the late 1950s the

[7] M Purshouse, *The Developing Scene in Active Techniques for Ship Noise and Vibration Control*, RINA Symposium 'The Future for Surface Warships' (London, 1990).

Looking up at propellers on a model destroyer in the Cavitation Tunnel at Haslar. The port propeller (right) is typical of a World War II design, with heavy cavitation from the blade tips, spreading down the surface, and from the boss. The starboard propeller is a five-bladed, noise-reduced design of the late 1950s, with the merest trace of cavitation. The speed would correspond to 12 to 14 knots.

Admiralty Experiment Works, Haslar, had developed and proved propellers free of cavitation at least up to 12 knots.[8] Since it is the suction on the back of the blade which provides much of the thrust, it cannot be eliminated. Sharp peaks of low pressure, which cause early cavitation, can be smoothed out by careful choice of section shape. The strength of the tip vortices can be reduced by reducing the blade loading towards the tip. A somewhat similar unloading is needed near the hub.[9]

Once cavitation has started, the noise can be attenuated by screening with air bubbles often discharged from holes in the blade. This is mechanically complicated since the air has to be

[8] David K Brown, 'Stealth and HMS *Savage*' *Warship 32* (London, 1984).
[9] David K Brown, 'Modern Propeller Design' *Warship International* 4 (Toledo, 1989).

brought down the propeller shaft and is even more complicated if the propeller is of the controllable pitch type.

At even higher speeds, turbulence in the water flow round the hull is the main source of noise. This source has been explored on ships towed at high speed: HMS *Penelope* was towed at 23½ knots, 6000ft behind the *Scylla* in 1971 in a series of tests.[10] It is possible, at least in the laboratory, to reduce turbulence in the flow, notably by injecting very long molecules, such as poly-ethylene oxide (Polyox), into the water close to the skin. This can have a marked effect on the drag; when it was tried on HMS *Highburton* in 1968 the frictional resistance was reduced by about 30 percent.[11] However, such substances are expensive and, it would seem, inherently slow to dissolve and hence are not likely to be a practical solution to turbulence noise. A more effective way of reducing noise transmission into the water is to lift the hull clear, as in a hovercraft. Noise ranging has shown that even current commercial hovercraft are very quiet.

Most of the techniques outlined here have been used in recent warships such as HMS *Norfolk*, the first Type 23 frigate, and her captain has said that she is the quietest surface warship of today. New ships are run over a noise range at various speeds while hydrophones record the sound over a very wide range of frequencies. Sometimes a fault is detected and remedial action is needed. Encounters with foreign ships enable a data bank to be built up of recordings of their noise signatures, aiding later detection and classification.

Radar Most yachtsman carry a radar reflector built up of plates at right angles in three dimensions (triple re-entrant corners) which will reflect a radar beam very efficiently back to its origin. Until recently, the superstructure of warships often incorporated such re-entrant corners, making their detection easy and helping radar guided missiles to home. The first step in reducing radar cross-section is to get rid of re-entrant corners where possible and ensure

---

[10] H John S Canham, *Resistance, Propulsion and Wake Tests with HMS* Penelope, Transactions RINA (London 1975).
[11] H John S Canham, John P Catchpole and Ron F Long, *Boundary Layer Additives to Reduce Ship Resistance*, Transactions RINA (London, 1971).

that those which remain do not include right angles. Only a few degrees away from the true 90 degree angle is required.

A polished steel ball will reflect a bright spot of light in whatever direction it is viewed. For this reason, curved surfaces in warships should be avoided above water; a flat plate will only reflect in one direction. It is strange that press releases show advanced warship studies for the US Navy with turtle-shaped upperworks.

Flat panels will reflect well in one direction, and therefore should not be vertical, so as to make life difficult for the sea-skimming missile. Flared hull sides reduce radar cross section as well as improving stability. References have been made to radar absorbing materials (RAM) but no information has been given on how well they work.

Finally, it must be remembered that missiles can home on the target's own radar emissions and that such radar signals can be detected at distances far greater than that at which the operating set can detect an enemy. Enemy radars can be jammed, screened by metal foil strips (chaff) or decoyed by reflectors released from the ship or hung from helicopters or balloons.

Infra-red Hot spots on a ship, producing an infra-red image, can be detected at considerable distances and may be used by homing missiles. The most important source of infra red is a ship's hot exhaust plume, and the infra-red image of this can be reduced by spraying the plume with cold water. At some loss of efficiency, and some increase in underwater noise, diesels can exhaust underwater, which may be a good solution. Paints also exist which reduce the emission of infra-red radiation.

The stealthy war is fascinating; concealment techniques are advancing rapidly and add much to the cost of a frigate. Success, moreover, is hard to judge in comparison with unfriendly powers. It is never certain whether an unfriendly ship's protective devices were in use when its signatures were recorded. A very low radar signature may be concealed by using radar reflectors in peacetime, and there may even be a 'magic' paint, to be applied just before war, which will reduce emissions from previously recognised levels. It is a subject on which little is published, and that little is often either out of date, an unsuccessful blind alley, or deliberately misleading. Low radiated signatures are nevertheless essential to the performance of an advanced warship and vital to its survival, despite the costs involved.

Seakeeping

As noted in Chapter 3, the Atlantic is rough even in the latitude of the Azores and is very rough indeed in the Greenland-Iceland area. The motion of the surface ship in bad weather degrades the performance of the ship, its weapons and, most of all, the ability of the crew to carry out their duties, both mental and physical. Submarines are also affected by the weather, mainly due to the background noise of the sea, but to a much lesser extent than the surface ship. To reduce this advantage, frigates require the best possible seakeeping.

'The way of a ship in the midst of the sea'[12] is proverbially difficult to define. It involves angular motions (roll, pitch and yaw) and linear motions (heave, surge and sway). Each of these six components of motion has an amplitude, a velocity and an acceleration. The interactions between the components are complicated and human senses are not well adapted to distinguish between them: for example, the brain will interpret acceleration in roll as an apparent angle, much greater than the actual roll angle (and so does a simple pendulum). Such complications mean that reports from sea need very careful interpretation; they are not often wrong but are often, inadvertently, misunderstood.

Based on questionnaires and studies at sea, limits acceptable to both machinery and crews for the various motions have been set in order that specific functions can be carried out. Limits are specified for weapon systems and their crews but, in some cases, these figures relate only to conventional ships and are not easy to read across to more novel forms.

Some typical limits for helicopter operation are given below.

TABLE 11: TYPICAL LIMITS FOR HELICOPTER OPERATION

Roll	2.5°
Pitch	2°
Vertical velocity	2 m/s
Lateral acceleration	0.25g
Vertical acceleration	0.15g

[12] *Proverbs* Chapter 30, verses 18-19.

These figures are single amplitude (one way) and are defined as 'significant' (that is, the value given is the average of the one third highest values, chosen because it matches closely the feel of an experienced observer).

Other limits used include: deck wetting – 30 times per hour; slams – 60 times per hour; and roll acceleration at bridge – $1.5\text{m}/\text{s}^2$ in sea state 5.

Helicopter operation is the most important task of an anti-submarine warship and is one of the most complicated.[13] Landing on is mainly dominated by the vertical velocity of the deck, though roll angle can also be important. In very severe seas it may be possible to land a helicopter by waiting for a lull, the so-called quiescent

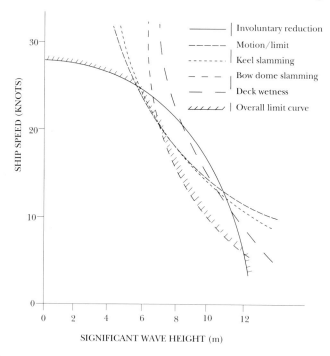

Figure 5/2: In low sea states the ship is slowed slightly by the added resistance of the waves. In higher sea states, the captain will decide to make bigger reductions in speed to reduce slamming, wetness or motions. The overall limit on speed is the lowest of any of the individual limits.

---

[13] Adrian R J M Lloyd and Peter J Hansom, *The Operational Effectiveness of the Shipborne Naval Helicopter*, RINA Symposium 'The Air Threat at Sea' (London, 1985).

period, though this always involves delay, and often risk. Manual task such as re-loading torpedoes and folding the helicopter tail etc are limited by lateral force (LFE), roughly equivalent to roll acceleration, while folding the rotor depends much more on wind strength than on sea state.

The speed of the ship will be reduced (or more power needed to maintain speed) by added resistance in small waves. In bigger waves, speed will be reduced more dramatically by the captain's deliberate decision on the grounds that the ship, or its sonar, may be damaged by slamming, that the motions are unacceptable or that there are too many green seas sweeping the deck (the so-called 'voluntary speed reduction'). Figure 5/2 shows the relationships.

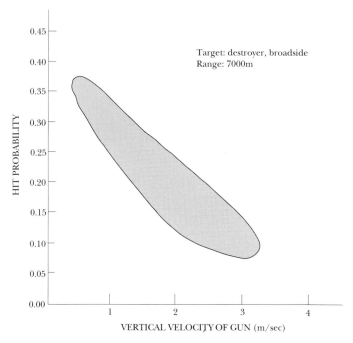

Figure 5/3: The probability of hitting a target with even a modern gun mounting reduces as its vertical velocity, due to ship motion, increases.

There is very little evidence of the performance of weapons in bad weather as practice missiles are scarce and are not generally fired in less than ideal conditions. Figure 5/3 gives some idea of how the accuracy of even a modern stabilised gun falls off when its support is moving.

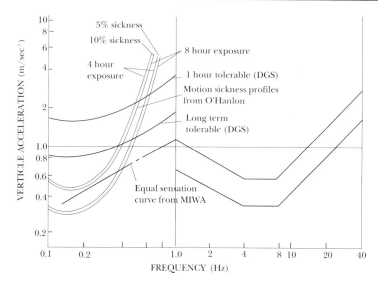

Figure 5/4: The curves to the left show different data on the tolerance of human beings to motion; those marked DGS are based on RN experience. Above a frequency of one Hertz, the curves define acceptable vibration levels.

The way in which human beings are affected by the weather is particularly complicated as it depends not only on what is currently happening to them, but also on what they have experienced before. The immediate effects depend mainly on vertical acceleration and its frequency: sea sickness[14] is most likely at frequencies between 0.15 and 0.30 cycles/sec (Hz) and will affect experienced sailors at about 0.8m/sec. What is less clear is the effect of motion on decision-making. Even if not physically sick, men are more likely to make the wrong decision or fail to take any decision when exposed to severe motions. The problem is a complicated one, is most important in smaller vessels, and has not yet been quantified.[15] Figure 5/4 shows some relationships.

A parameter, 'Subjective Motion Magnitude' (SMM), has been derived from experiments in the USA on human volunteers to combine the physical effects of acceleration and frequency. On this

---

[14] It is no coincidence that the word 'nausea' derives from the Greek word for 'ship'.
[15] David K Brown, 'Fast Warships and their Crews', *The Naval Architect, Small Craft Supplement* (London, 1984), see also:
David K Brown and Paul M Marshall, *Small Warships in the Royal Navy and the Fishery Protection Task*, RINA Small Fast Warship Symposium (London 1978).

scale, RN trials have shown that a value of SMM of 12 is about the limit in the short term; with somewhat less evidence it is suggested that a value of SMM of 4, averaged over the year, is the long-term limit above which motion becomes intolerable. This is about that experienced in the Island class offshore patrol vessels or in the similar Flower class corvettes of World War II.

Sailors have long advised 'One hand for yourself and one for the ship'. In this computer age this, too, has been measured. The need to stop the job and hang on depends on the lateral force, and is measured as the Lateral Force Estimator (LFE) or the closely related Motion Induced Interruption (MII).[16] While still a student, Monk derived criteria for acceptable rolling based on LFE which are used by the Ministry of Defence.[17]

Almost all RN ships have active roll reduction fins. Their performance depends on the effectiveness of the control system, usually set to reduce roll amplitude. Above about 10 knots a typical frigate installation would reduce RMS roll from 8° to 3°. Some improvement may be possible by using the controls to minimise lateral force rather than amplitude.

Overall, rough seas cause a loss of effectiveness as shown in Table 12 in a 3000-tonne frigate.

This table is based on medical reports and on discussions with very experienced seamen officers and though it suffers from the limitations of all generalisations, it does give as good a picture as is possible of the effect of bad weather on fighting efficiency.[18]

One may carry this argument a little further. It has already been suggested that a value of £100,000 per day may be attached to an operational day at sea for a frigate. Using the table above, a *Leander* class frigate will be ineffective for the equivalent of 13 operational days (out of 150 at sea) due to motions and this can be valued at £1.3 million. In an extreme case, the war might be lost while the ship is ineffective.

There are a number of things which can be done to reduce this loss of operational value. Most of these measures cost money, some quite a lot, but the loss of value, £1.3 million (£10.5 million, Net

[16] Adrian R J M Lloyd, *Seakeeping* (Chichester 1989).
[17] Karl Monk, *A Warship Roll Criterion*, Transactions RINA (London, 1987).
[18] David K Brown, 'The Value of Reducing Ship Motions' *Naval Engineer's Journal* ASNE (Washington, 1985).

TABLE 12: EFFECT OF BAD WEATHER ON A 3000-TONNE FRIGAT̶ (NORTH ATLANTIC)

Sea state	Time (%)	Significant wave height (m)	Max speed (knots)	Roll (°)*	Roll (stabilised) (°)*	Pitch (°)*	Heave (m)*	Effect	Loss of effectivene̶ (%)
1-4	39	≤2.5	27	3½	≤2½	1	0.5	(1)	0
5	31	2.5-4	24	4½	3	1½	1	(2)	10
6	21	4-6	20	6	4	2	1.5	(3)	30
7+	6	6+	<10	14+	9½+	2½	2	(4)	95

Effects: (1) Nil

(2) Inconvenience, work takes longer, some effect on sensors, RAS difficult.

(3) Up to one third crew sick, sleep difficult, all exhausted, helicopter operation difficult. many weapons systems degraded.

(4) Ship is ineffective as a fighting unit.

* RMS values

Present Value) is real and a full investment appraisal would clearly show the need to reduce the effects of motion.

The first step is to use surface ships in areas where the sea is kind to them. A frigate is more effective in the Azores than off Greenland, adding strength to the arguments for a southern strategy for the surface fleet. Some figures based on USN experience[19] derived in a slightly different way from the previous table show the effect of latitude on helicopter operability (see Table 13).

Helicopter operability can always be improved by moving the

TABLE 13: EFFECT OF LATITUDE ON HELICOPTER OPERABILITY

Latitude	Operable time %	
	Winter	Summer
0	80	90
30	50	80
60	10	50

[19] Colin Kennel and Brian White, *Innovative Designs for North Atlantic Operations*, Transactions SNAME (New York, 1985).

landing spot to a position close to amidships, where the motions are least (see Figure 5/5). Such an arrangement is not easy to achieve with the other constraints on the upper deck layout of a frigate but some ideas, shown in the next chapter, have gained approval from operators.

Simply making the ship longer helps (see Figure 5/6). A 108-metre frigate will lose the equivalent of 13 days operational time, while increasing the length to 125 metres reduces the lost days to 7. If the equipment is not increased in the longer ship the extra cost will be due to structural steel at about £10,000 per tonne, a total of £1.7 million, which will be offset over the life of the ship by the improved fuel economy of the finer ship (about 550 tonnes per year).

An even greater reduction of motion is offered by the SWATH (see Appendix 1). It is never easy to compare unlike concepts and with SWATH it is necessary to think very clearly whether the comparison is to be made with a conventional ship carrying the same weapon fit or with a much larger monohull giving the same seakeeping.

In 1978 the US Coast Guard carried out a seakeeping trial in which the 200-tonne prototype SWATH *Kaimolino* was matched against conventional Coast Guard vessels, one of 100 and the other of 3000 tonnes. During one run the *Kaimolino* had a maximum pitch of 2° and a roll of 2° (both out to out) and a maximum vertical acceleration of 0.08 gravity, figures which were marginally better

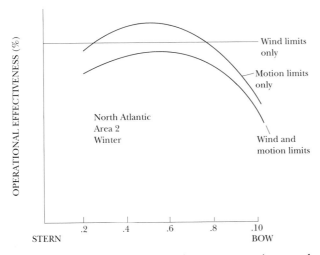

Figure 5/5: This diagram shows that helicopter operations can be carried out most effectively, more days per year, if the landing spot is just abaft amidships.

than those recorded by the 3000 tonne ship some fifteen times her size (Pitch 3°, Roll 5-6°, acceleration 0.08g) and vastly better than the smaller cutter (8°, 16°, 0.27g).[20]

Conscious of the problem of comparison, Kennel *et al* [21] created three frigate studies, the baseline (a conventional monohull to carry the same payload at 26 knots in calm water an with good sea-

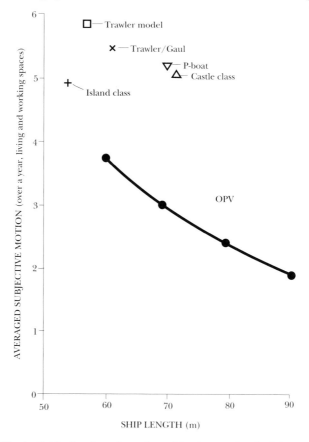

Figure 5/6: The individual points show the subjective motion in living and working spaces, computed for real ships whose performance is known, averaged over a whole year's weather pattern. (Note that the Castle is the World War II corvette). The curve shows values, computed in the same way, for design studies of the Castle class OPV, of differing lengths.

[20] Jerry L Gore, 'SWATH Ships' *Naval Engineer's Journal* (Washington, 1985).
[21] Colin Kennel and Brian White, *op cit.*

keeping by normal standards), a SWATH with the same payload and engines and a 'seakeeping' monohull to match the rough weather performance of the SWATH. Comparative details of these vessels are given in Table 14.

TABLE 14: SWATH COMPARISON			
	Length (m)	Displacement (tonnes)	Calm sea speed (knots)
Baseline	136.5	5330	26.6
SWATH	114	6950	25
Seakeeping	186	9030	26

The engines were two LM 2500 of 48500shp (41225Kw) in all studies.

TABLE 15: SWATH COMPARISON – MOBILITY			
	Baseline	SWATH	Seakeeping
North Atlantic, all year	91	96	97
Northern North Atlantic, all year	87	94	94
North Atlantic, winter	83	92	93
Northern North Atlantic, winter	76	88	89

Limits on motion were selected governing speed, helicopter operation, sonar performance, surface and AA warfare. Tables 15 and 16 illustrate the operability of these vessels as a percentage of time at sea.

TABLE 16: SWATH COMPARISON – HELICOPTER OPERATION			
	Baseline	SWATH	Seakeeping
North Atlantic, all year	89	95	95
Northern North Atlantic, all year	84	92	93
North Atlantic, winter	80	90	91
Northern North Atlantic, winter	71	84	85

It can be objected that the figures for helicopter operability are too high because no account is taken of wind speed. Even an air base ashore in the northern North Atlantic area would have difficulty in achieving 84 percent operability. However, even in southern latitudes the SWATH shows an impressive improvement in operability over the baseline ship.

The cost of SWATH vessels is considered in Appendix 1, but in this example the SWATH is appreciably more expensive than the baseline ship, but much less than the ship with equivalent seakeeping. The main difference is in the structure.

TABLE 17: SWATH COMPARISON – STRUCTURE AND COST

	Structure weight (tonnes)	Increase (tonnes)	Extra cost (£million)
Baseline	1834	–	–
SWATH	2365	531	5.3
Seakeeping	3782	1948	19.5

Similar difficulty is experienced in comparing the seakeeping of advanced naval vehicles (hydrofoils, hovercraft and so on) with monohulls. At the same all-up weight, about 200 tonnes, the accelerations shown in Table 18 might be expected on the bridge when travelling through 1.5 metre waves at 30 knots.

TABLE 18: ADVANCED MARINE VESSEL SEAKEEPING COMPARISON

Type of vessel	Acceleration x g (gravity)
Conventional (eg Fast Patrol Boat)	0.16-0.18
Side wall hovercraft (SES)	0.20
Hovercraft	0.05
Surface piercing foil	0.04
Submerged foil craft (Jetfoil)	0.02
SWATH	0.03

Speed

High speed is always useful to a warship, but the cost of obtaining it is such that a more moderate speed is usually chosen. The minimum requirement is to have a margin in hand over merchant ships which the warship might have to escort. Since only a few merchant ships can exceed 20 knots, their escorts need 25 or a little more, though CVS escorts will need at least 30 knots. A rule of thumb for a 4500-tonne frigate is that one extra knot will add 90 tonnes to the displacement and £2 million to the cost.

Higher speeds can be obtained by hovercraft and hydrofoils and a number of arguments, many fallacious, are put forward to justify fast craft. It is often said that high transit speeds will reduce the number of vessels needed but the consequences of the loss of one of the smaller force might be severe. It is also said that fast craft are needed for anti-submarine warfare using the 'sprint and drift' mode, stopping to listen and dashing off to pursue the contact. If a towed array or dunking sonar is used, however, the time to reel it in becomes a major factor in determining the mean speed of advance.

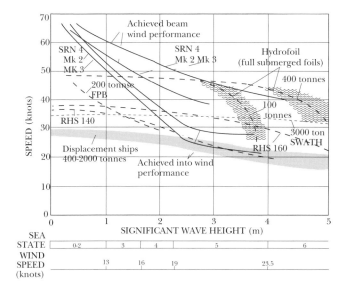

Figure 5/7: The speed achieved by some marine vehicles in different wave heights. Note that the performance of the hovercraft, with air propellers, depends on wind speed and direction. The SRN 4 is a cross channel hovercraft, and the RHS 140 and 160 are Rodrigues hydrofoils.

HMS *Speedy*, a Boeing Jetfoil, used to explore various roles for hydrofoils, including fishery protection, where she was very successful.

Speed can be valuable; when the hydrofoil *Speedy* was used for fishery protection her high transit speed meant that fishermen did not know where she was and her approach speed was such that she was alongside 10 minutes after coming over the horizon, allowing no time to change illegal nets.

In general, however, high-speed warfare at sea is best left to aircraft. Apparent exceptions should be examined very critically.[22]

Hull form

It must never be forgotten that the proportions and shape of a ship are the outcome of, and not the input to, the design process, and as such are the response to operational requirements. The naval architect does not start with a preconceived idea of what is 'right'

---

[22] William D O'Neill, 'Advanced Naval Vehicles: Who Needs Them?', *Marine Technology* 14-4 (Washington, 1977).

and then fit his design into it. The so-called 'Short-fat' ship contro-versy[23] in the United Kingdom was only able to drag on so long because politicians and the media failed to understand the nature of design. The ministry's naval architects were not advocating long thin ships, but rather an approach which led to fairly long frigates; the same approach led to relatively short and fat LPDs and MCMVs.

Starting from a conventional baseline frigate, it will be found that increasing length will reduce pitch and heave in head seas and, for frigate operating patterns, will reduce overall fuel consumption. Layout, particularly of the upper deck, will be improved. The rela-

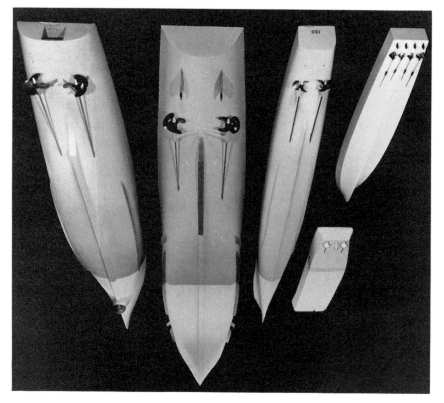

Right for the job; there is no single 'right' form. These models, not to the same scale, are (left to right) an MCMV, a carrier, a destroyer, a fast patrol boat and a landing craft, and all right for their intended role.

[23] *Warship Hull Design Inquiry* (London, 1988).

tive motion between the stem and the wave surface will increase and greater length must be accompanied by increased freeboard if the ship is to remain dry in a seaway.

Length will increase the loading on the structure in waves and, as a rule of thumb, the length/depth ratio should not exceed 14. The need to strengthen the structure in order to keep stresses to an acceptable level means that adding length is more expensive than adding beam. However, the extra cost in structural steel at £10,000/tonne as worked into the ship is largely offset by reduced fuel costs, and the other benefits can be seen as a bonus.

To keep a ship dry, it must have adequate freeboard. While the desirable value of freeboard depends on many factors, including speed, it has been found that the simple rule Freeboard = $0.6\sqrt{}$ (length m) is perfectly satisfactory for the preliminary design of frigates. Fine tuning, using model tests or computed motions, can be applied later. Discussions on bow shape raise almost theological heat, but most naval architects would agree that very considerable bow rake is desirable. The magnitude of flare and the value of knuckles is much more controversial. I designed the form of the Castle class, which are very dry [24] mainly due to their freeboard, enhanced by bulwarks. They have a knuckle and very considerable flare, possibly overdone (see Figure 2/2).

There is only a narrow range of suitable values for beam; there must be enough for stability, but too much will lead to rapid rolling with high lateral accelerations. It is well to start a new design near the upper acceptable limit of beam as the inevitable growth high up will always tend to reduce stability.

A deep draught forward is needed to reduce slamming in head seas, and for sonar immersion, while draught aft is needed to accommodate the large propellers required for quiet propulsion. Using conventional dry docks and blocks it is found that the diameter of the largest propeller which can be fitted to a twin screw ship is about equal to the draught.

The thoughts expressed above lead to a slender ship (low block co-efficient) with fine sections. It will be found that practical constraints, such as fitting the awkward corners of gearboxes, maga-

---

[24] David K Brown, 'Service Experience with the Castle Class' *The Naval Architect* (London, 1983).

zines and thrust blocks within the hull, prevent any extremes of slenderness – though an awkward corner can sometimes be given a blister rather than altering the whole hull.

The naval architect can then adjust a number of parameters in the search for fuel saving or reduced motions. Such changes may each give only a 1 percent improvement, but it is not difficult to make enough changes for their sum to be important – all too often a number of parameters are simultaneously 1 percent out, and the degradation is serious.

A flap or wedge under the transom has been common in fast craft for many years but it has taken a very long while for its value to frigates to be recognised. A large flap angle will reduce resistance at high speed and increase it at low speed, but the effect on propeller efficiency is more complex, generally allowing a bigger angle with benefits at all speeds. The gain can be considerable; in one trial top speed was increased by about a knot and fuel consumption reduced by 6-8 percent. A smaller, but worthwhile, gain would be more typical. It is probably true that flaps are most effective if the hull has an unfavourable shape due to other design considerations or if the ship has put on a lot of weight during its life.[25]

---

[25] Gabor Karafiath and Steven C Fisher, 'The Effect of Stern Wedges on Ship Powering Performance' *Naval Engineer's Journal* (Washington, 1987).

6

The Cost of Ownership

There are a number of features of warship design which are specifically aimed at reducing the cost of ownership. This may sometimes involve an increase in first cost.

Reduced manning

The declining birth rate in the late 1960s and 1970s means that there are now fewer young people available and a smaller proportion of them seem to want to go to sea. The Royal Navy has recently accepted that women (WRNS) can serve at sea even on combatant ships but the numbers available will also be small (for this reason I hope that 'man' and 'manning' will be acceptable terms). Even when the people are available, their accommodation is still very expensive. Manpower is both scarce and costly and it is essential that warships operate with smaller crews. The tasks which are most demanding in manpower are:

☐ Action Information Organisation (AIO)

☐ Damage control

☐ Replenishment at sea

☐ Ship husbandry

☐ Catering and hotel services

Reduced manning in any of these tasks is almost bound to cause some penalty, but is reduction is essential, as it seems to be, much can still be done to minimise such penalties.

The manpower demands of the AIO are, to a considerable extent, the result of the requirement to operate in a manual mode following damage or breakdown. The provision of a second AIO reduces the need, and the performance of modern weapons makes a manual mode of little value. Since the AIO must operate continuously, manned in three watches, any reduction in operators is trebly welcome. Indeed, it may well be argued that the extra cost of a duplicated AIO, called for to reduce vulnerability, may by offset by savings in manning if both are automated and the manual mode of operation abandoned.

Though the Falklands war showed the advantage of big crews, particularly numerous technical ratings, in damage control, it can be argued that 'damage control' is of lesser importance in a truly redundant ship. Automatic fire suppression systems, such as the Graviner system, should be used extensively, saving manpower and reducing the risk of serious fires. Redundancy of whole systems would mean that a major compartment, flooded or burning, could be abandoned without completely sacrificing the ship's fighting capability. Men will, however, still be needed to contain the effects of damage and it seems certain that there will inevitably be some increase in vulnerability of ships with reduced crews.

A very long endurance ship could do away with the requirement for replenishment at sea, while a smaller crew would reduce the need for provisions.

The ship husbandry task of day-to-day cleaning, painting and low-level maintenance is demanding and cannot be eliminated, though dirt is created by people and small crews will make less. Major cleaning can be done by contractors on return to port. By avoiding dirt traps in the design and using easy-clean surfaces the task can be reduced, though many such 'easy-clean' materials are fire and smoke hazards.

More attention should be given to organising the crew into small communities, the original meaning of 'mess', cleaning and maintaining their own living and working area. To some extent, this should also apply to officers; they should be responsible for keeping their own quarters clean and tidy.

There seems no advantage in a general move to precooked airline meals, though there may be advantage in using this approach to reduce the need for catering staff to provide meals for watch keepers at unusual times. Virtually all book-keeping and administration should be done ashore.

The design of frigates is usually dominated by upper deck layout (see figure 4/3) and the minimum length so defined will have space below for about 100 men. The cost of their accommodation is relatively small, little more than that the furnishings, cooking and sanitary fittings. If the ship has to be made bigger to carry more men, the cost will increase at about £100,000 per man, much more than the cost of building a first class hotel room in central London. On economic grounds, there is little justification for a crew less than the baseline figure of 100, a level at which any degradation of operational performance would be small. Smaller crews are possible, though the savings in crew cost must be carefully balanced against that of automation, including maintenance. It might be cheaper to pay a sea-going allowance to persuade sailors to go to sea.

Margin policy

Since the life of a warship is of the order of thirty years from the start of design studies, it is clear that some capacity for extra equipment is necessary. In addition, a design margin is needed because modern warships almost always complete overweight due to errors in data and to new requirements. Finally, weight will increase due to the authorised and unauthorised addition of new equipment, extra stores and paint. For example, *Leander* grew 87 tons in eight years, made up of 40 tons of paint coatings (up to eighty coats in places), 40 tons of stores and only 7 tons of authorised fittings.

In the late nineteenth century, battleships had only shallow armour belts and it was important that they floated close to the design draught or much of the value of the belt would be lost, as happened to the overloaded Russian ships at Tsushima. It became standard practice to include a weight margin in the design, the use of which required the authority of the Board. This is a practice continued today, with margins both on weight and on the height of the centre of gravity above the keel (KG). These margins are considered under three headings:

☐ The Design Margin caters for errors and uncertainty in data and in the design process. The size of this margin depends on the degree of novelty in the ship and its equipment, and the wise designer conceals part of this margin so that it is not subjected to arbitrary cuts. It is interesting and a little surprising that ships designed in the United Kingdom and in the United States just after the Washington Treaty completed considerably lighter than the design figure; this is almost unheard of today.

☐ The Board Margin is to allow the Staff limited freedom to add essential extra equipment either during building or when the ship is in service. The formal accounting of such additions imposes a discipline on the Staff which is valuable but, since there is no space margin, there is a degree of artificiality in the Board Margin. In a tightly cash-limited ship, there is little scope for extra equipment, and hence the formal Board Margin is less important.

☐ The Growth Margin allows for growth in service, which experience shows is about 0.5 percent of the displacement per year.

British practice is that the ship must meet all performance requirements with both Design and Board margins fully used, accepting that growth will cause degradation, while safety requirements must be met at all displacements from that without margins to that with all margins used, including growth.

Space margins are more difficult and are rarely allocated explicitly. A distributed space margin such as extra wide passages is often not usable when needed. A space marked 'margin' on the plans will soon be usurped, and even concealment as 'recreation space' is usually revealed as pressure on the design increases.[1] USS *Spruance* was designed with exceptionally large margins, making it possible to use the same hull for the *Kidd* and *Ticonderoga* classes. However, *Ticonderoga* completed with little or no margin.[2] On the other hand, some extra equipment is vital. When the crew slept in hammocks, it was usually possible to squeeze them up[3] to fit in more 'Black

---

[1] The Tribal class frigates had, for some time, a margin concealed as 'Royal Marines Mess Deck'. This disappeared when the First Sea Lord, inspecting the drawing remarked, 'I didn't know these ships carried Marines. What a good idea!'

[2] J Lehman, *Investigation of* Ticonderoga, House of Representatives Committee on the Armed Services, (Washington, 1982).

[3] Students of physics may feel that the old style mess deck obeyed the Gas Law - Pressure x Volume = Constant.

Boxes' and their operators, but this is virtually impossible with modern living quarters and standard furniture.[4]

In modular design, soft areas, such as store rooms or mess decks, should be arranged adjacent to electronic spaces where demand for more space is most likely; this approach can in fact be adopted even without modular design. If the ship is designated with a minimum superstructure and adequate stability margins, it will be possible to reposition the displaced spaces in new deckhouses. In some cases it may be possible to design a ship with a parallel middle body and add an additional section at refit ('Jumboise') or to replace the existing section with a larger one.

The most serious problem with growth in service is loss of stability. Hull sides flared throughout the length can do much to improve matters in this respect. It will not usually be possible to incorporate sufficient flare to maintain stability completely as top weight is added, but at least degradation will be slower. To some extent, a variable-incidence transom flap can be adjusted to reduce the loss of speed or endurance consequent on weight growth. There is usually a small margin on crew numbers in the design complement and margins on electric power supply and chilled water are also usually provided.

Margins of any kind lead to a bigger ship with increased first cost, and are frequently the subject of arbitrary cuts. Nevertheless, experience shows very clearly that a ship without margins is unsatisfactory on completion and a headache ever after. The correct approach is to insist on a margin at the design stage and to control the addition of new equipment through an effective cash limit though this, too, should have a small, covert margin.

Maintainability

The through-life cost of frigate is at least three times the cost of procuring it, and reducing the cost of ownership should therefore concentrate on running costs. In addition, the utilisation of the ship should be as high as possible. The typical 20-year life of a current Royal Navy frigate may be broken down as shown in Table 19.

Maintenance of the hull has been greatly reduced in recent class-

---

[4] Harry D Ware, *Habitability in Surface Warships* Transactions RINA (London, 1986).

TABLE 19: LIFE OF A FRIGATE

Status	Years
Available	
At sea	5.5
In harbour but active	3
Giving leave	2.5
Not available	
Refits, trails, etc	5.5
Programmed and unprogrammed maintenance	3.5
TOTAL	20

es by better initial preparation of the steel, improved paints, the extensive use of sprayed metal coatings and by cathodic protection. Much of the reduction in numbers in the Royal Dockyards is due to the consequent reduction of refit work. Most machinery is exchanged for refurbished units rather than refitted on board or in the yard. This saves much time and some cost, offset by the cost of refurbishing units and by the need to have more units within the fleet.

There is probably not a great deal more that can be done to improve overall maintainability, through access could still be better and rust traps eliminated. Individual machines, weapons and systems all fail from time to time, and the recent Ministry drive to improve reliability even at the expense of first cost must be welcomed.

Modularity

Modular design and modular building are phrases commonly used and almost as commonly misunderstood. Modular building, or advanced outfitting as it is sometimes known, is now virtually standard practice and will be discussed first.

Traditionally, the bare hull of a new ship was launched and taken to a fitting-out berth, where all machinery, armament and equipment was installed. Everything had to go in through hatches and

---

TABLE 20: COST OF SHIPYARD WORK[5]

Location	Cost factor
Prefabrication shop	1
Unit assembly	5
Building slip	10
Afloat	20

---

along narrow passages, obstructed by frequent doors and coamings. Such a process was lengthy, costly and frustrating (see Table 20).

In modular building, the structure is first assembled in the prefab shop into fairly small units, and even at this stage some systems, such as pipes, are installed. These units are then assembled into a large module, usually a transverse slice of the ship, weighing some 250-300 tonnes.[6] The module hall is warm and clean and with both ends of a 24 metre module open, it is easy to install all fittings and most systems. For example, in HMS *Argyll*, the second Type 23, 9500 items were installed before launch and 90 percent of cables were run, so that she will complete 19 months after launch instead of the 27 months needed for *Norfolk*. *Lancaster*, the fifth ship, should show a further advance. This style of building also levels the peak labour loading which used to occur late in outfitting and which added much to delay and cost. Planning and supervision are also much easier in a module hall than afloat.

Modular design involves designing major systems, particularly weapons and sensors, in large 'boxes' which can be assembled and tested remote from the ship and then dropped into place. The big advantage is that the design of the weapon system can be de-coupled from that of the ship, so that they can be progressed in parallel rather than sequentially. The converse problem is that the dimensions of the box must be large or there will be an unacceptable constraint on the weapon designer and there must be a very strong control over the interface.

---

[5] Sir Robert W S Easton, *Modern Warships – Design and Construction* CEI Prestige Lecture (Glasgow, 1983).
[6] David K Brown, 'The Duke Class Frigates Examined' *Warship Technology* No9 (London, 1989).

A Type 23 module for HMS *Argyll* being moved into position on the building slip at the Yarrow yard.

At this interface, services such as chilled water, electric power (usually at a range of frequencies) and others pass from ship to box. The arrangement of these connections has to be standardised and can impose constraints on both weapon and ship designer. Obviously, there is little problem in packaging an existing weapon system, though, since it will have to use the next largest box, there may be some increase in size.

It is sometimes suggested that boxed systems enable a rapid change of role for the ship, but this is rarely possible. An ASW ship has different requirements for signature reduction from those of an AAW ship, even to the extent of a different machinery fit. Antennae also differ and masts may be in the wrong place. Boxed systems do make it easier to replace defective equipment and will usually help in replacing a Mk I version with the Mk II. It is hard to believe that modular design would have helped in replacing Sea Slug, with horizontal missile stowage, by Sea Dart, whose missiles are stowed vertically in a drum.

There are three well-publicised modular systems in NATO. The smallest box is in the British 'Cellularity' system[7] with maximum dimensions 1.7m high, 2.0m long and 0.75m deep. These are arranged in cells, compartments whose dimensions are multiples of the box size (with clearance). The cells have standardised runs of services, and access routes are sized to pass the boxes. Cells are arranged next to soft spaces (store rooms, mess decks and so on) so that it is quite easy to enlarge a cell during the life of the ship provided that there is somewhere for the displaced space to go. Cellularity is used to a limited extent in the Type 23 in that access and some spaces are of cellular dimensions.

The Blohm und Voss Meko system uses much larger boxes, up to 4.5m long and 2.44m high, and these are usually dropped into holes in the deck. The advantage is that a single design of hull can have different combinations of weapons. The use of Meko has generally been confined to the installation of existing, well-developed weapon systems.[8]

NAVSEA's SSES[9] is a more elaborate system, in which great care and attention is paid to configuration control and interface design. It has been used for several major systems in the USS *Arleigh Burke*, and this has led to a mistaken impression that it is limited to very large modules and big ships. The principle is valid for smaller ships and developments in that direction are in hand.

Cellularity has the greatest flexibility during the long transition phase while most systems still have pre-modular dimensions, but is has fewer advantages in testing and tuning complete systems than the other two schemes.

Most modular design systems were developed prior to the general introduction of modular building, which has reduced their value in new construction. UK government policy is against major midlife modernisation, again reducing the value of boxed design, through cellularity would be of value in the limited updates still found necessary. Collaborative designs, such as the abortive NATO NFR 90, will rarely lead to identical requirements from all the par-

[7] P Jonathan Gates and Simon C Rusling, *The Impact of Weapon Electronics on Surface Warship Design* Transactions RINA (London,1982).

[8] R Meller, 'MEKO Ships from Blohm and Voss' *International Defence Review* 5 (1979)

[9] Thomas E Burt, 'Combat System Integration in the USN' *International Defence Review* 1 (1986)

ticipating countries, and a modular approach seems very desirable to give flexibility in weapon fit.

A number of proposals have been made for containerised weapon systems, including search and tracking radars, which can be dropped on to a merchant ship for self-protection. By the time that proper command systems and data links to other ships are added, such systems will be expensive and their capability will be limited by the lack of signature reduction and the very poor vulnerability of the merchant ship. Training, too, will be difficult. It therefore seems that expensive weapon systems should be mounted in real warships.

The US Navy developed a containerised helicopter support system called Arapaho which could be used to convert a container ship into a carrier very quickly. A prototype set was leased by the Royal Navy and used for some time on the Royal Fleet Auxiliary *Reliant*. At a displacement of 31,500 tons, she carried five Sea Kings. In general, it was thought that this system saved little in either time or cost in converting a helicopter carrier.

7

The Introduction of Advanced Technology

Both the Royal and United States Navies have recognised the need for technological progress, and because of the many formal collaborative programmes and informal contacts at all levels, there is a great deal of common ground despite fundamental differences in approach. The US Navy, inspired by the vision of Admiral Metcalf as Deputy Chief of Naval Operations (Surface), has adopted a high profile, top-down approach under the banner of 'Revolution at Sea'. The British style is bottom-up, with a large number of small steps joined into a loose 'Advanced Technology Warship' programme. Not only are many of the technical problems the same but so, too, are the political impediments. Much of the work can and will be shared, and other allies may also participate.

The Revolution at Sea[1]

New weapons and an explosive growth in technology in response to a similar growth in the perceived threat have forced navies to re-examine their roles and the way in which their tasks are carried out. The surface ship battle space used to be fixed by the 20-mile range of a battleship's guns, the height to which an anti-aircraft shell could reach and the depth of a few hundred yards of old Asdics.

Today's battle space extends to the range of a cruise missile (1200 miles), to the altitude limits of a guided missile (100,000 feet) or even that of a satellite at 23,000 miles, and to the depth limits of modern submarines, some thousands of feet. The changes which are necessary are as difficult to navies as to individuals.

---

[1] Admiral V J Metcalf, 'Revolution at Sea' *Proceedings* USNI 1/88 (Annapolis, 1988).

Admiral Metcalf has observed that 'to anticipate and prepare for change means moving from the familiar and well-understood to something more dimly perceived ... Hence, individuals who occupy positions of power and have most to lose will resist change, as will bureaucrats who strive to maintain the current order'.

To implement the Revolution at Sea, two study groups have been set up, with a '3-star' steering group, 'Group Mike'. The Surface Combatant Force Requirements Study is to investigate the numbers and types of surface combatants which the navy will need during the next quarter century.

The Ship Operation Characteristics Study is an 'examination of the policies and factors that form the foundations of the Navy, from war fighting to ship construction. The study group will examine the operational requirements that drive ship characteristics. It will look at the policies which for a millenium have implicitly or explicitly determined the way we build and operate warships'.[2]

Admiral Metcalf offers as an example (and it is an issue that seems to preoccupy him) the need to re-examine the requirement for navigation bridges and visual signalling, which are spacious, costly and add to radar echoing area. It is interesting to note that the Royal Navy tried to abolish the bridge at the end of the pre-Dreadnought era, when HMS *Agamemnon* was built with a tiny walk-way round her armoured conning tower; a normal bridge was soon added. Similarly, the early post-World War II anti-submarine frigate conversions (Type 15) had no bridge but had a periscope in the operations room. The last few were fitted with a conventional bridge.

Some of the early output from these studies will be discussed below. The Royal Navy has been reviewing its operational policies in a series of 'concept and sub-concept' papers, some of which have been illustrated by ship design studies, but the link between future operations and design does not seem to be as well co-ordinated as it is in the United States.

Problems and prejudices

In 1840, the brilliant French Naval Architect Dupuy de Lôme noted

---

[2] *Ibid.*

that the then novel iron ships gave rise to 'beaucoup de préjugés, de doutes raisonables et des difficultés réelles'. The introduction of new technology today equally gives rise to prejudice, reasonable doubts and some real difficulties. At a major meeting on future design policy, Royal Navy and US Navy representatives saw their common problems as:

☐ Failure to make clear the vital contribution of vehicle technology (referred to in the United States as HME – Hull, Machinery and Electrical) to fighting value;

☐ Lack of a proper investment appraisal procedure by which additional first cost can be offset by savings in through-life cost, (the specific case of the 'cash limited' ship is too often raised as an insuperable barrier to progress);

☐ Insufficient resources to complete an R & D programme and validate the results;

☐ Insufficient time to complete technology development and integrate the results into the whole ship system during the time-scale of a typical ship acquisition programme;

☐ Lack of a coherent and integrated ship technology strategy (in particular, costs tend to fall on one department while the benefits appear elsewhere, causing bureaucratic problems in budgeting);

☐ Following from the above, a lack of clear authority for introducing innovative technology or responsibility for a cost-effective and adequately funded programme;

☐ A widespread impression that ship technology is fully developed and hence that there is little prospect of worthwhile improvement (investment appraisal would soon show the fallacy of this argument);

☐ The contractual difficulty of directing a shipbuilder to use a specific artefact or procedure since, should it fail, the contractor's responsibility for the whole programme is diminished; and

☐ Finally, a basic resistance to new technology, which is seen as an unnecessary risk to budgets and schedules (all too often, a new idea will be criticised as unproven, often with the unspoken implication 'and we don't intend to give you a chance to prove it').

Success and failure

Since World War II, the Royal Navy has had many successes in innovative technology, offset by only a few failures. A brief review of some of these programmes may give some pointers for the future. The first success may be seen as the frigate design programme in the early 1950s. In ship technology the novel aspects of the new design were seakeeping and the structure.

The seakeeping features were based on the experience of the designer N G Holt, a keen yachtsman, refined and developed by model tests at the Admiralty Experiment Works (AEW) at Haslar, then directly controlled by the Director of Naval Construction (DNC). The form was not quite in accordance with thinking based on more modern theories, but the performance in service of *Whitby, Blackwood* and their sisters has been so good that modern designers have difficulty in equalling, let alone improving on, their performance.

The structure was based on the experience of full-scale explosion trials by the Naval Construction Research Establishment, at Dunfermline (NCRE), also under DNC control. This led to a structure with thin plating and closely spaced longitudinal stiffeners. While this was successful in its primary aim, such a structure also proved expensive to build and prone to corrosion in service. With more experience, it was possible to develop a compromise structure, well able to resist explosions and cheaper to build and maintain.

Another novel feature in the anti-submarine frigates was the effort made to reduce underwater noise. The first step was to lower the shaft rotational speed using advanced (by British standards) double reduction geared steam turbines. AEW, with a very small team, then used a mixture of advanced mathematics, model tests, ship trials and ad hoc modifications to develop a successful quiet propeller.[3] Typically, these propellers, introduced from about 1960,

---

[3] David K Brown, 'Stealth and HMS *Savage*' *Warship* 32 (London, 1984).

remained free of cavitation up to 12 to 14 knots, compared with the
6 to 8 knots of wartime propellers. The programme was controlled
by a small working party, with all directly concerned reporting to a
high-level steering group which had the will and authority to get
things done.

One may also mention the development of active anti-roll fins.
These were pioneered by Denny-Brown in the mid 1930s and fitted
to many ships during the war. The early installations were of limited
value and after the war DNC and the manufacturers carried out a
series of trials on HMS *Cumberland* to improve the control system.
Another important advance was made in the use of non-retractable
fins, which took up very little space, in place of the much more
hydrodynamically efficient, high aspect ratio retractable fins (which
were very demanding in space, weight and maintenance).

Other technological developments in ships can only be mentioned briefly, but include high-copper anti-fouling paint (161P)
and the development of the 'plastic' (GRP) warship. On the engine
side, the successful introduction of the gas turbine was the most
notable advance, together with a range of noise reduction and
shock attenuation measures.

There are few failures to discuss. One such was the delay in
accepting and using the new self-polishing anti-fouling paints. Most
commercial operators were convinced by the evidence within some
three years of the new paint's introduction. The Ministry, however,
failed to recognise the value, and the real, but solvable, health
problems were used as a bargaining counter in Dockyard pay negotiations. Since such paints have been introduced it has been found
that they save at least £750,000 in fuel bills per ship over a three-
year period and are very long lasting. These paints raise some interesting questions on environmental issues: the toxin – tri-butyl tin –
is poisonous to many marine organisms and the paints have been
condemned for this reason. On the other hand, the fuel saving
reduces carbon dioxide release to the atmosphere, thus helping to
reduce global warming.

There has also been very slow acceptance of the value of transom
flaps in frigates (see page 103). Such flaps were introduced in the
mid 1950s on fast patrol boats and it soon became clear that they
could be tuned to improve frigate speed while reducing fuel consumption. This was eventually confirmed by model tests and, finally, in 1988, by a ship trial. In a Type 21, a saving of about 5 to 6 per-

cent in fuel consumption, together with about a knot increase in top speed, can be expected. Benefits in other classes would be a little less but the cost of installation is very small.

The main lesson seems to be that a small, high-level directing group is essential if more than one department is involved. This is needed to give authority to the decisions of a more junior working party. It also seems clear that the major part of the ship research programme must be firmly controlled by designers, a point made very clearly in the United States by Dr Reuven Leopold,[4] though resources should still be available for some speculative work by the research teams. Research is not a discrete entity, and the separation of all research from design and building poses impossible problems when budgets are limited; how does one judge, for example, between seakeeping and laser weapons? Both are essential and the real balance to be drawn is between through-life cost and effectiveness in each area.

The Advanced Technology Warship Programme

The Royal Navy's Advanced Technology Warship Programme was originally created in an attempt to overcome the real problem of introducing novel ideas in the limited timescale of a new design. It was intended to produce a 'mail order catalogue' of new artifacts and procedures which had been proven in prototype or model and which could be introduced in full confidence into a real design. Inevitably, such a catalogue threw up other ideas which were not fully proven or even studied and it became clear that a second volume would become a framework for an R & D programme. Ideas, proven or developing, could apply to all aspects of the ship and its systems.

The final stage of each study is to look at its impact on a real ship, and there are many cases where incorporating a number of changes may be relatively more or less cost effective than single steps.

As an example, one such study was based on the role of the Duke class (Type 23) frigate. It should be emphasised that this study illus-

---

[4] Reuven Leopold, 'Innovation Adoption in Naval Ship Design' *Naval Engineer's Journal* (Washington, 1977).

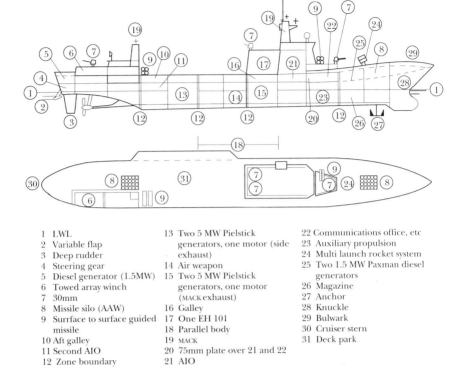

1 LWL	13 Two 5 MW Pielstick	22 Communications office, etc
2 Variable flap	generators, one motor (side	23 Auxiliary propulsion
3 Deep rudder	exhaust)	24 Multi launch rocket system
4 Steering gear	14 Air weapon	25 Two 1.5 MW Paxman diesel
5 Diesel generator (1.5MW)	15 Two 5 MW Pielstick	generators
6 Towed array winch	generators, one motor	26 Magazine
7 30mm	(MACK exhaust)	27 Anchor
8 Missile silo (AAW)	16 Galley	28 Knuckle
9 Surrface to surface guided	17 One EH 101	29 Bulwark
missile	18 Parallel body	30 Cruiser stern
10 Aft galley	19 MACK	31 Deck park
11 Second AIO	20 75mm plate over 21 and 22	
12 Zone boundary	21 AIO	

Figure 7/1: The Advanced Technology Frigate described in the test, generally equivalent to a Type 23.

trates what could be achieved with technology available today, applied to an existing Staff Requirement. It is not a fully worked-out design, but is thought to be realistic.

Many of the ideas incorporated in this study are aimed at improving the ability of the ship to fight, and naval architects can do much by reducing the number of days per year in which performance of equipment or crew is degraded by the ship's motions. The first step is to bring the helicopter landing spot closer to amidships, reducing the vertical motion due to pitch. Helicopter decks are traditionally at the aft end because it was the only space available in the early conversions and was very convenient to arrange in new ships.

It is not easy to rearrange the cramped upper deck layout of a frigate, and the task is made more difficult by the understandable dislike felt by pilots of a second superstructure behind them when landing. Several schemes have been looked at, and that shown in

Figure 7/1 seems viable and acceptable to pilots. The landing deck is sponsoned to port, the normal direction of approach, while the small, carrier style after superstructure is on the starboard side. This will allow operation on more days per year than the conventional arrangement.

The draught has been increased considerably to enable operation at higher speeds without slamming. Bulwarks are used rather than rails except in way of the landing deck. Bulwarks help to keep the ship dry, conceal many upper deck fittings which contribute to radar echoing area and, perhaps most important, require less maintenance. Wetness is further reduced by using a keel anchor as in SSNs and by incorporating a knuckle.

Low-speed handling in following seas has sometimes caused handling problems in frigates, and a possible solution, as shown, would involve a cruiser rather than a transom stern. The post-war survey ship *Vidal* was given a cruiser stern for this reason. This feature is, as yet, unproven and would require model testing. For the same reason, very deep rudders are installed.

The ship is designed to be more 'battleworthy'[5] than ships in service. Fighting ships must be able to survive damage, and not only survive but also 'fight hurt'. The basic approach is 'concentrate, duplicate, separate', as outlined in Chapter 5.

Diesel-electric propulsion is very suitable for this design style since a considerable number of generators can be distributed over the ship. Some have underwater exhausts, others above-water, so that either noise or infra red signature may be reduced as appropriate to the operational situation. So far, no satisfactory alternative to a rudder aft has been devised; bow rudders are virtually useless in normal manoeuvring. A possible, but unproven, scheme is to use a Voith-Schneider auxiliary propulsor forward.[6]

The main operations room is forward, under the mainmast to reduce the length of wave guides, and is protected by 75mm plate, which will keep out most splinters and many small arms projectiles. A secondary operations room is arranged aft to control the after

[5] David K Brown, *The Battleworthy Frigate*, Transactions NECI (1990).
[6] The uncompleted German aircraft carrier of World War II, *Graf Zeppelin*, was to have had two retractable Voith Schneider units forward for propulsion and manoeuvring if the propellers and rudders were damaged. They were never tried but should have worked, at least if the conventional rudders were not jammed hard over.

weapon systems only. It will use the same hardware and software as the main room, though with fewer consoles, so that the extra cost is kept down.

The ship is divided into five battle zones, each with its own power supply; bulkheads between zones are double skin, sandwich material to resist blast and splinters. Accommodation for each rank and category is divided fore and aft so that one hit is unlikely to kill a high proportion of a key group.

Subdivision aft is improved by raising the towed array gear to the upper deck. The structure is designed so that the ship will hold together even after much of the section is destroyed.[7]

The cost of ownership is reduced by the fuel-efficient diesels and by optimising hydrodynamic aspects. A variable incidence flap is arranged aft to minimise fuel consumption at all speeds and displacements. The shaft brackets are angled to improve the flow into the propellers. The shafts are of carbon reinforced plastic, light and strong, designed to survive severe whipping damage.

The design style features a minimum superstructure with little more than the hangar, sensor supports and compass platform forward, and a generator and towed array winch aft. Generous access lobbies are included which will accept many of the minor fittings usually placed in the open, so reducing maintenance and radar signature.

A parallel middle body is arranged to facilitate a 'Batch II' with different requirements. It might even be possible to modernise the ship by cutting out the old parallel body and replacing it with a pre-assembled unit with different equipment.

Such a ship will clearly be bigger and cost more than HMS *Norfolk*. Few of the novel features are very expensive, however; most merely involve extra steelwork, which is cheap. Some contribute to reducing operating costs, and the use of commercial diesels will further help in offsetting increased costs elsewhere. The biggest cost increase arises through provision of a second operations room, but the additional cost of duplicate circuit boards and of software cannot be enormous. There will be extra cost in installation, testing and tuning, but such cost must be accepted; a ship without a secondary nerve centre has little ability to fight hurt.

---

[7] David K Brown, *op cit* (n5).

It must be reiterated that this frigate is not suggested as a real ship. It is sketched to demonstrate the application of a variety of new technological developments to a conventional ship. These developments are better utilised in the more radical designs outlined in Chapter 9.

8

The Fleet Mix

The paralysis which afflicted the Argentine surface fleet after the sinking of the *Belgrano* by HMS *Conqueror* in the Falklands war shows that the nuclear attack submarine is today's capital ship. The SSN is also a very potent ASW vessel and, as suggested, it should play the major role in Northern Barrier operations. Infrastructure costs for the submarine force, such as building and refitting yards and training, are heavy, and therefore the total force costs are not very sensitive to small changes in numbers. In consequence, it would seem that every effort should be made to keep the force at its present level; it is most regrettable that the July 1990 cuts should have fallen so heavily on the SSN force.

A central theme of this book is the need to increase the number of aircraft at sea, both fixed-wing and helicopters. The three CVSs of the *Invincible* class are versatile ships and the only British ships capable of operating fighter aircraft, the VSTOL Harrier. The requirements of Harriers for maintenance and for weapon storage and support are very considerable, and there can be no prospect of dispersing the aircraft in small numbers round the fleet. The ski jump ramp considerably increases the payload of these aircraft and can only be fitted to fairly large ships. The CVSs will also carry out full maintenance on helicopters carried in frigates with limited facilities. The ratio of Harriers to helicopters can be varied slightly.

Three such ships are sufficient to ensure two available for operations, provided that there are enough Harriers. It must be a matter for concern that these large and very valuable ships are fairly easy to disable, though their subdivision should keep them afloat after considerable damage.

Their role in major war would be as the core of a trade protection force, providing command and control, limited AEW, air support and maintenance for helicopters embarked in small ships.

They have the capability, shown in the Falklands, of leading a strike force in minor wars, worldwide. They can also be adapted as personnel carriers if not committed to other tasks, making them valuable in disaster relief.

They will not need replacing for many years, but it is not too early to think of the characteristics needed in the next generation. Their weakness is the lack of high-performance fighters, and with the short takeoff and landing run of new planes such as the European fighter, it may be possible in future to envisage a true carrier of CVS size (it is most unlikely that funds will permit anything bigger in the Royal Navy).

Nuclear power is quite feasible for ships of this size and would have considerable advantage in reducing the size of the uptakes, which are such an obstruction in the hangar of the current ships; there would also be more volume available for aircraft fuel. On the other hand, nuclear power is politically unpopular in many countries and its adoption would limit the worldwide use of the ships. Multiple diesel-electric propulsion may be the best compromise, particularly if underwater exhausts can be used. Seakeeping is not a great problem in ships of this size, so this reduces the advantages of SWATH which, at this size, would be hard to dock in the United Kingdom.

The Government has stated a requirement for two aviation support ships (ASS) carrying helicopters to support amphibious operations. They are envisaged as based on merchant ship practice, probably new construction, and considerably more elaborate than the £70 million training ship *Argus*. There are many technical problems, discussed later, in designing such ships to be both cheap and effective. However, such ships should be versatile and flexible in deployment.

There remains the possibility of a refuelling platform (using platform in its true sense, instead of in the incorrect sense as a synonym for vehicle), which would be a large tanker with a flat top used to refuel shore-based fighters in the Norwegian Sea or elsewhere. Such a platform would have no command and control facilities, except those necessary for directing the landing of aircraft, and no stowage or maintenance facilities, though accommodation for a few spare pilots might be useful. Provided that the temptation to escalate the design to that of a full carrier is resisted, such a vessel would not be expensive to procure or operate. The training of

RAF pilots in deck landing might, however, be a problem.

The most difficult and technically interesting aspect of the fleet mix is the composition of the destroyer and frigate force. The House of Commons Defence Committee confirmed in June 1988[1] that fifty such ships are the minimum needed for the Royal Navy's peacetime tasks and, at that time, this figure was committed to NATO by the United Kingdom, replacing the older promise of seventy. In July 1990 the Government announced that the frigate force would be reduced to forty – followed a few days later by the Prime Minister's announcement that an additional frigate would be stationed in the West Indies to assist in the fight against drugs. In August, Iraq invaded Kuwait and additional RN frigates were sent to the Gulf. There can be no right number of ships, but forty is very low; it can be considered adequate only if the force is kept up to date by regular replacement and operated intensively.

Like other defence equipment, the real cost of frigates has risen since World War II by about 7 percent per annum. The Type 23, HMS *Norfolk*, has broken this trend due to effective political control of cost, the introduction of improved building techniques such as advanced outfitting and, not least, by a clever design, led by the RCNC. Most of these features are one-off, and it seems inevitable that the Type 23 price, said to be about £110 million, will be the new baseline for rising cost. The pressures to increase capability and hence cost are inexorable; the Royal Navy's air defence version of the ill-fated NATO frigate would have been much more expensive than the Type 23 and the proposed UK equivalent can be no cheaper.

On the future, reduced budget, it will not be easy to sustain even forty conventional frigates, while at the same time more ships are needed in the light of the reduced detection ranges against the new, quieter Soviet submarines. There can be no solution; there is no point in building large numbers of small and ineffective ships and equally no sense in having a very few powerful ships, too few in number to cover all tasks. This is discussed by Khudyakov,[2] who points out that one may optimise for maximum effectiveness at

---

[1] House of Commons Defence Committee, 6th Report *The Future Size and Shape of the RN Surface Fleet* (London, 1988).

[2] L Y Khudyakov, *Analytical Design of Ships* (Leningrad, 1980).

constant cost or for minimum cost at constant effectiveness. Carried to extremes, he sees the one leading to what he aptly calls the Super Battleship Paradox, the other, emphasising numbers at the expense of capability, to the Chinese Junk Paradox. One may, however, wonder if the Royal Navy's Flower class of World War II was so limited in capability that it fell into the latter category.

A few years ago, Admiral Zumwalt of the US Navy proposed what he called the HILO mix, with a few very capable ships and a larger number of ships capable of performing a more limited range of tasks, though quite effective within those limits. It was not a new idea; the fleets of Nelson's day consisted mainly of third rate, 74-gun ships, with only a few of the big first rates. A more recent example is the Royal Navy's mix of *Whitby* and *Blackwood* anti-submarine frigates after World War II. They carried identical anti-submarine sensors and weapons, but the *Whitby* had a gun armament and better command and control together with some three knots more speed, making its cost about twice that of a *Blackwood*. It was intended to build one *Whitby* to two *Blackwood*s, but the latter's capability was too narrow for peacetime operation, and building stopped after the first twelve. The *Whitby* was developed through *Rothesay* to the even more successful *Leander*, which was built in considerable numbers for the Royal Navy and other navies.

Since the frigate's main offensive capability lies in its helicopter, the aim must be to maximise the number of helicopters at sea. Current frigates, Types 22 and 23, can operate one medium helicopter (EH 101) or, in earlier ships, two Lynxes, so that forty frigates means about forty helicopters in the frigate force. (The CVSs and AORs will carry additional aircraft).

The effective life of a frigate is about twenty years before obsolescence, fatigue cracking and corrosion make it too expensive to support.[3] Simple arithmetic shows that a steady building programme averaging two ships per year is needed to keep the force at forty ships. Taking a mean of 4000 tons displacement between the type 23 and the bigger AAW ship to follow, there must be a building programme of 8000 tons per year and, if the simple assumption is made of constant cost per tonne, this tonnage could be redeployed

---

[3] David K Brown, 'The Geriatric Frigate' *Warship World* (Liskeard, 1989).

into one 6000 tonne destroyer with four helicopters and a corvette of about 1800 tons with one EH 101.

In some years, it might be desirable to build four corvettes and create a force of about fifteen destroyers and thirty-five corvettes, restoring the old figure of fifty hulls, but with ninety-five helicopters. There may be a slight saving on ship cost, but money must be found for the additional helicopters. No price has been agreed for the EH 101, but a UPC[4] of £20 million will be assumed, and some corvettes would have to be dropped from the programme to pay for them. This simplistic approach ignores the wastage of helicopters in accidents, the cost of training and so on, and a more realistic strength might be some forty-five ships deploying ninety helicopters.

There are problems, mainly political, with the HILO mix. The House of Commons Defence Committee itself has admitted

> We find yet more compelling the more cynical argument that once a cheaper alternative to a fully capable frigate began to be ordered, such ships would not be ordered in greater numbers, but would take the place of frigates, changing the nature and capability of the whole fleet.

This is powerful argument, put forward by MPs wise in the way of Government. However it is even less credible that the Government will absorb the rising cost of frigates, all other defence hardware, and maintain even the reduced the forty ship frigate force. It has also been argued that the corvette is below the threshold of capability; this will be debated below.

There can never be enough MCMVs to meet a determined mining campaign, but the task can be reduced by the use of fast route surveillance craft. These will seek out routes free of mines, rather than looking for and disposing of the mines themselves. Such a tactic can only be used on a favourable seabed, but it will reduce the load on the more conventional minehunters.

Government plans for the amphibious force have yet to be finalised, but discussions centre on two aviation support ships, two LPDs and six LSLs. The present ships of the amphibious force are, to a considerable extent, the unplanned residue of previous capa-

---

[4] Unit Production Cost; roughly what is paid to the prime contractor.

bilities, but since only those ships relevant to current operations have been retained, the balance is fairly good. At the time of writing (1990), there are two assault ships, *Fearless* and *Intrepid*, five LSLs, two smaller LCLs, and a commitment to replace the aviation support ship, *Hermes*. Studies suggest that a near one-for-one replacement is the most cost effective procurement strategy.

Dolton and Silvia[5] describe a detailed study into the composition of the future amphibious force carried out in 1982, in which three force structures were examined:

☐ As now, two LPDs, six LSLs and two ASSs;

☐ Four standard ships, combining LPD and LSL, with two ASSs;

☐ Four big standard ships, including ASS capability.

In the first option the LPD was of similar size and capability to the existing ships, and could carry either four LCUs or two of the US Navy's LCACs, together with two Mexiflote mobile pontoons, and four LCVPs would be carried in davits. The LSLs would be generally similar to *Sir Galahad*.

The standard ships of the second option would each carry two LCUs, four LCVPs and two Mexiflotes in a dock. Those of the third option would carry the same small craft but would be bigger – about 20,000 tonnes – with four helicopter spots. These ships approach Graham's idea, described below, of 'Carriers of Large Objects'.[6] Rather surprisingly, they were not envisaged as having a through deck, and could only accept Harriers in the vertical mode. The authors conclude in favour of the first option, and Ministerial statements imply that this is current UK government policy.

The programme might be as follows:

☐ Buy or convert one ASS, with a second to follow much later;

☐ Life extension programme for one existing LPD, and build

[5] J C Dolton and P Silvia, *Concepts for a UK Replacement Amphibious Fleet* RINA Symposium 'Warship 86' (London, 1986).

[6] Clark Graham and Michael Bosworth, *Designing the Future US Naval Surface Fleet for Effectiveness and Producibility* SNAME Symposium on Ship Production (New York, 1989).

one new one (if the remaining hull life on the existing ship is adequate); then

☐ Convert three existing old LSLs as *Sir Tristram* and replace the sixth as *Sir Galahad*.

The older, extended-life, ships would be replaced by new units over a long timescale. In principle, the scheme seems excellent, retaining or even increasing the existing capability while spreading the cost over a long period. In Chapter 10 some of the inherent problems of ship design are discussed and possible solutions indicated.

The amphibious force is at its most vulnerable when loitering off Norway. A possible alternative would be to hold the force in Scotland or the Orkneys and move it when required, using high speed craft. A superficial study some years ago showed that the SRN 4 cross-Channel hovercraft could transit from Aberdeen to Northern Norway at 65 knots, refuelling in the Trondheim area, while carrying a useful payload. Bigger hovercraft or high-speed craft would be needed to make this approach truly viable, and the high development and procurement costs could only be justified if run in parallel with a commercial programme.

It will be noted that this fleet mix is based on a naval budget which is constant in real terms at today's (1990) level, some 20 percent below that of earlier years. With the reduced threat from the Warsaw Pact, it seems likely that overall defence spending will, however, fall still further, though since the Navy's commitments will reduce less than those of the other two Services, it may suffer less. Moderate cuts can be met by 'salami slicing', that is, ordering slightly fewer of each category. If a bigger cut is imposed, the amphibious capability as a whole should be examined, since its cost, including its own escorts, is high in relation to the end product of two Marine Commandos onshore. It could also be seen as the most provocative element in a relatively peaceful world.

9

Future Warships

This chapter will consider the specific design problems of the various categories of ship which make up the Royal Navy or which might be added to that navy. Alternative designs are proposed which might offer improved capability within the same total budget. The designs discussed below have not been developed in any detail, but should be sufficiently accurate to provide an insight into the problems facing the designers of future warships for the Royal Navy.

Cheap aircraft carriers

It does not seem likely that the Royal Navy will ever be able to afford fleet carriers of the size operated by the US Navy, or even the smaller, fixed wing carrier represented by the cancelled CVA-01 of about 50,000 tonnes. The three *Invincible* class CVSs should continue to operate for many years, perhaps to a total life of thirty years. However, there seems to be every intention that replacements should be built eventually, and it is not too early to consider the main factors affecting the design of such ships.

The basic problem is the cost of the ships and their aircraft. It would cost about £300 million, perhaps more, to build an *Invincible* today, and new requirements would make a replacement even more expensive. It is likely that political factors will keep the ship price below £400 million. On top of this comes the cost of the aircraft, say eight fighters at £30 million and twelve helicopters at £20 million; this gives a total of about £500 million, and further aircraft will be needed for wastage. One ship with its aircraft and weapons will cost about £1 billion, an investment which needs protection by all possible means of active and passive defence. For this reason, there can be no really cheap aircraft carrier, and the suggestions which follow merely offer alternative ways of maximising capability.

The very large uptakes and downtakes of the gas turbine seriously obstruct the hangar and lead to a big island in the *Invincibles*. Nuclear power might be the best technical choice but, as noted above, will probably be ruled out on political grounds. Diesel-electric propulsion would be more expensive to procure than gas turbines but this would be offset by lower fuel consumption and smaller uptakes, and the engines could be dispersed to reduce vulnerability.

By the time the replacement CVSs enter service, there should be a number of fighter aircraft available which could make a conventional take off and be able to land on a ship of about 20,000 tonnes. An alternative would be much higher performance developments of the VSTOL Harrier. In either case a flight deck length of 220m, with a ramp, seems desirable.[1] On about 20,000 tonnes, such a ship could carry eight advanced fighters (European Fighter Aircraft or F-18A derivatives), three AEW helicopters (EH 101s), and nine ASW helicopters (also EH 101s).

Rolling take-off with a ramp would not permit simultaneous landing and take off, but with such a small aircraft complement this should not present any serious operational difficulties. Two centre-line lifts would be provided as the ship would be too small for side lifts.

Operationally, the fighters would be able to destroy shadowers, to disrupt small attacking formations and to launch strikes against lightly defended targets on sea or land. The helicopters would have similar, but updated, capability to that of the early Merlins.

At £3 billion for a minimum force of three of these ships, the programme will be expensive, but it is essential if the Royal Navy is to operate away from shore-based fighter cover. If engaged in war, these CVSs may be hit. Ships of this size will tolerate considerable damage without sinking, and separated machinery should give a reasonable probability of retaining some mobility. Their most vulnerable aspect will be the C^3I facilities, and there is an argument for removing these from the CVS and carrying them on a destroyer.

---

[1] A R Hamilton & J M Crawford *Supersonic STOL A/C Carrier* University College Postgraduate Design Study (London, 1987). My thanks are due to the Professor of Naval Architecture for permission to use this report.

Even in these days of closed-circuit television, however, there is much to be said for the commander briefing and debriefing of pilots face to face, and the best comprise is likely to put the main command on the CVS with a secondary command in a destroyer.

Helicopter carriers

Though the design of a relatively cheap helicopter carrier poses fewer problems than that of a fighter carrier, the value of its aircraft both in cash terms and in their importance to the success of an operation means that some resources must still be expended on defence for the ship itself. The great success of the escort carrier (CVE) in World War II suggests that it is easy to build a hangar and flight deck on top of a merchant ship and obtain an effective warship. Though the modern helicopter does not need the take-off run of wartime plane, it is very much bigger:[2]

	Swordfish	*EH 101*
Weight (kg)	4,200	14,200
Length (m)	10.9	22.9
Width, folded (m)	5.2	6.0
Aircraft crew	2-3	6
Maintenance crew	2	13

It must also be appreciated that the best wartime escort carriers, such as the *Casablanca* and *Commencement Bay* classes, were quite far removed from simple merchant ships, particularly in their subdivision and in the protection of fuel and weapon stowage.[3]

For a simple helicopter carrier there are two main configurations: one with a big hangar forward[4] and a flight deck on the same level aft (as shown on page 134), and the other the classic carrier configuration with a hangar below the flight deck and two lifts to

---

[2] David K Brown *Armed Merchant Ships, a Historical Review* RINA Symposium (London 1987).
[3] David K Brown 'Development of the British Escort Carrier' *Warship 25* (London 1983).
[4] The hangar must be forward with doors facing aft to avoid intolerable draughts with doors open if they faced forward. Forward facing doors are also exposed to impact damage from seas.

carry the aircraft (see page 135). The advantage of the first configuration is its economy; there is less structural work and no expensive lifts are required. Such an arrangement is limited to aircraft complements of less than about six since re-arrangement of aircraft within the hangar is difficult for larger numbers. Care must also be taken to ensure that the landing spots are not located too far aft where the pitching of the ship is more keenly felt, though this is less significant in an amphibious support ship operating in sheltered waters. This layout precludes the use of fixed-wing aircraft except in the vertical take-off mode when their payload is negligible.

The classic carrier layout demands two lifts since one may break down or be damaged, and lifts to transport an EH 101 are expensive. Hangar layout is simple and, as the flight deck will be long enough for VSTOL aircraft, it will be worth fitting a ski jump so that Harriers can be refuelled. Full support of Harrier operations, however, requires considerable space, equipment and manpower and should not be contemplated on anything less than a CVS.

Such simple helicopter carriers can be envisaged with between six and eighteen aircraft. The value of the payload, however cheap the ship, provides ample justification for both active and passive defensive measures, which cause the cost to escalate rapidly. For this reason, it seems likely that cheap helicopter carriers will be limited to carrying a small number of aircraft, say between six and twelve. To some extent, force vulnerability can be reduced by spotting helicopters on a number of ships, though if they rely on the carrier for maintenance its loss will still be very embarrassing.

A cheap helicopter carrier with the hangar forward and the flight deck aft on the same level. Moving aircraft around the hangar is difficult if more than about six are carried.

A cheap helicopter carrier with a flight deck and lifts. More convenient – and costly – if a larger number of aircraft are carried.

If six aircraft are considered sufficient, the forward-hangar design would be preferable on the grounds of initial cost. The advantage of an alternative landing and refuelling deck for VSTOL aircraft seems, however, to be conclusive in favour of the classic carrier design; as usual, the bigger ship seems more cost effective, so a mini-carrier of conventional design, with helicopters, is the more likely choice.

It is often suggested that these ships should be built to 'merchant ship' standards, but there are many aspects of merchant ship design and equipment which are unsuitable for even a simple warship. Many of these problems can be overcome at very moderate cost in a new design, but cannot be remedied in an existing ship. For a start, the hull must be made of reliable, tough steel. The Royal Navy learned a subtle, but vital, lesson in the cold of the Arctic during the World War II convoys to Murmansk. At low temperatures shipbuilding steel became brittle and cracked and these cracks could spread quickly in welded ships; hence the otherwise inferior rivetted British-built ships were preferred for the Murmansk convoys as the seams would usually stop cracks from spreading.

Following similar cracking problems in early postwar ships (*Vengeance* in Operation Rusty, 1947) steels were introduced in warships which are ductile and tough at low temperatures, even under explosive loading. The steel used in merchant ships is not tested for low temperature toughness[5] and could fail under sudden loads. Notch tough steel does not cost much more than the basic material and seems almost essential for ships to operate on NATO's northern flank, though this virtually rules out the conversion of existing ships.

Cast iron, normally used for hull valves in merchant ships, though better today than in World War II, is still likely to break under shock loading. Subdivision also needs to be designed to warship standards. In particular, the merchant ship practice of fitting watertight doors low down in machinery spaces in unacceptable; bulkheads should be unpierced below the intact waterline and preferably below the likely damaged waterline.

Merchant ship fire mains are usually kept dry and filled only when used; hence they can be made of mild steel. A warship, and particularly a carrier, needs fire-fighting water instantly available and fire mains kept permanently full of salt water must be made of more expensive cupro-nickel. Weapon stowage and aircraft fuel stowage also need some protection, at least against accidental fire.

The most effective signature reduction measures are quite cheap; it is the elimination of the last decibel which is expensive. Simple noise mounts, reduced-noise propellers and sloping superstructure sides are comparatively inexpensive and effective. Such simple signature reduction measures make the use of decoys more valuable, though to be really effective, some AIO facilities are needed. A carrier requires sufficient equipment to control landing and take off, but operational control is better vested in a destroyer of the escort. Lastly, a carrier needs a number of small guns for the sake of morale and to prevent hijacking.

Such a ship would cost about one third to one half of a CVS and in terms of cost per aircraft is not particularly good value. As noted above, cost-effectiveness studies will always favour the bigger ship and only fleet modelling against realistic scenarios will show the advantage of larger number of cheaper vessels, particularly for fairly small navies with a limited budget. The cheap Harrier carrier has been dismissed rather cursorily, but a study by Honnor and

---

[5] John D G Sumpter, John Bird & John C Clarke, *Fracture Toughness of Ship Steels* Transactions RINA (London, 1988).

Andrews[6] shows clearly how much space is needed for workshops, weapon stores and their test facilities and weapon lifts, together with the personnel to operate them. Such facilities are quite uneconomic to provide for a few aircraft and if more than a few are carried the ship becomes a high-value unit needing at least the survivability of a CVS.

Though I have suggested strongly that replenishment of frigates at sea be given up, it will remain necessary to replenish the CVS with aircraft fuel and probably stores such as sonobuoys. Some thought has been given to combining the tole of AOR and mini carrier and, indeed, the ships shown on pages 134 and 135 both had replenishment variants. It will only be possible to install replenishment rigs on one side of a vessel and even then there will be interference with flying. In general, it seems better to keep the roles separate and limit the AOR to a platform aft and a hangar for three to four helicopters with limited maintenance facilities.

The refuelling platform

The refuelling platform is a rather different concept and is envisaged as a flat top on a big tanker, on which land-based fighters can land and refuel; it can thus be seen as a replacement for the scarce and expensive tanker aircraft. Many new fighter aircraft such as the 'European Fighter Aircraft' and the F-16 have short landing and take-off runs, and a deck of only 220m is adequate, though as at most airfields, one or two emergency arrester wires would be fitted. Such a platform would hang well back from a task force or screen, refuelling fighters en route to their operational areas.

Without adding to the cost, a deck part for four to six planes could be provided, though maintenance would increase rapidly if they were exposed to salt water for any length of time. It might also be possible to arrange for a change of pilot. The biggest problem to such an approach lies in the need to train all RAF pilots in deck landing. There would also be an interesting debate over which Service should pay for the facility. Such landing platforms could aid

---

[6] Arthur F Honnor & David J Andrews *HMS* Invincible - *The First of a New Genus of Aircraft Carrying Ships* Trans RINA. (London, 1982).

long-range deployment of fighters, though a properly-equipped
base would still be needed within reasonable range. The ship would
have no military equipment except for approach radar and its ability to survive would be no greater than that of a big tanker.

The 6000-tonne destroyer – first generation

The primary role of a 6000-tonne destroyer would be to lead ASW
operations with its four large helicopters and to command and control a force including older frigates and corvettes as well as maritime patrol aircraft (MPA) and SSNs. It should have the capability
to defend itself and ships in company against air attack, using
FAAMS.[7] At 6000 tonnes, such a vessel can be designed as a double-
ended ship, able to move and fight, at least to some extent, after a
single hit.

The design is dominated by the big hangar. The cheapest solution is to have the hangar forward with a rear door giving access to

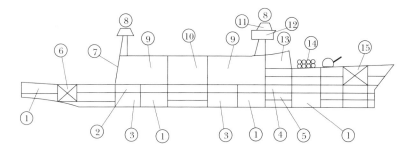

1 Diesel generator	9 Two EH 101s
2 Second AIO	10 Lift
3 Motor	11 Phased array radar
4 Communications office	12 Bridge
5 AIO	13 Electronic warfare offices
6 Missile silo	14 Surface to surface missile
7 Door to hangar	15 Missile silo
8 MACK offset to starboard	

Figure 9/1: A 6000-tonne destroyer (DDH) intended to carry four big helicopters.
The MACKS are to starboard, giving a clear run for Harriers to the ramp on the port
side.

[7] Norman Friedman *World Naval Weapon Systems* (Annapolis, 1989)

a flight deck aft (somewhat similar to that shown on page 134). This is awkward in practice, involving a lot of helicopter movements, and the flight deck tends to be shifted too far aft as the design progresses, particularly when the arrangement of weapons is considered. The preferred arrangement is the mini carrier, shown in figure 9/1.

Aircraft operators rightly object to arrangements which are dependent on a single lift, whose failure might put all the aircraft out of action. Figure 9/1 is a compromise; there is only one lift but rear doors to the hangar give access to an alternative landing spot on the quarter deck which can be used, at least in favourable weather. It is likely that three helicopters would be sufficient to ensure one on station at all times, but a reduction in numbers would not affect ship cost significantly. The fourth helicopter offers a good chance that two will be available at all times, and also makes it easier to rotate helicopters with the corvettes for maintenance.

Admiral Metcalf, in his *Revolution at Sea*, called for a bridge 'no larger than a 747 cockpit'[8] and this has been provided as a crow's nest on the forward mack. Both masts are to starboard, leaving an unobstructed flight deck. Since this is long enough for Harrier take-offs, a ski jump is provided. It is not intended that the destroyer should be capable of operating Harriers, but there may be occasions when a refuelling platform, some considerable distance from the carrier, is valuable, and the destroyer would fulfil this role.

The combination of a big hangar and a long flight deck raises the same problems which were apparent in World War II aircraft carriers. If the hangar sides and flight deck take the main load, there will be a major discontinuity in the depth of the hull girder at the ends of the hangar, which would lead to failure under the whipping loads due to an under-keel explosion. On the other hand, the deeper section amidships could be of value under the same loading. The alternative would be to support a flight deck on steel portal frames with GRP cladding on the sides. More detailed analysis of the design is necessary before a firm conclusion can be reached.

The hangar, flight deck and quarterdeck are open, making the ship very adaptable to other roles such as troop carrying or disaster relief. The open quarterdeck could carry small landing craft, inflat-

---

[8] Admiral V J Metcalf, 'Revolution at Sea' *Proceedings* USNI 1/88 (Annapolis, 1988).

A basic corvette for towed array operations, with a flight deck aft for an EH 101. It is based on a stretched and refined Castle.

ables or vehicles. One or more helicopters could be landed to provide space for troops or evacuees in the hangar.

The machinery is diesel electric as detailed above and all the 'advanced' features mentioned in Chapter 7 are included.

The baseline corvette

The baseline corvette is a development of the Castle class (shown on page 43) and it will have the same excellent seakeeping qualities and small superstructure. Its primary role will be to deploy a towed array and to provide a landing deck for a big helicopter. For this role it will have to be quiet, and therefore it will be fitted with diesel electric propulsion.

A speed of about 25 knots seems desirable to keep up with container ships and it will be necessary to use lighter structure[9] than the Castle to obtain a satisfactory form. The power curve shows that the Castle needs at least 50 percent more power than the *Blackwood*

---

[9] The hull form of the Castle class OPVs was loosely based on the *Blackwood* but as the OPV put on weight at constant, or reducing, length due to the use of cheap but heavy structure, the power requirement rose dramatically (see Figure 9/2). A faster Castle would need lighter structure.

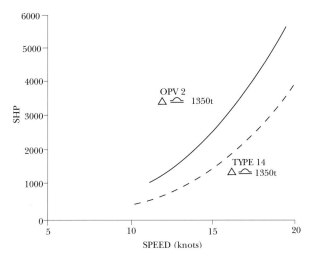

Figure 9/2: The long, light hull of Type 14 needs much less power than the cheaper, heavier hull of the Castle, particularly at higher speeds.

of the same displacement at 25 knots. Both noise reduction and speed add to the cost but are affordable since costing is estimated on the basis of frigate cost per ton.

These corvettes will have a peacetime role in offshore protection, for which they will need a gun capable of destroying a terrorist or pirate launch and which is accurate enough for a close warning shot to be fired. A modern 30mm has some anti-helicopter capability, but a larger gun such as the ROF 105mm[10] may be preferred. These relatively simple weapons may be containerised and changed to suit the task.

In a major war the corvette would operate as a towed array ship, up to 100 miles from a destroyer or carrier, and its helicopter would use the bigger ship for major maintenance and to avoid the worst consequences of being kept in the open. For many peacetime tasks the helicopter would not be embarked. A folding hangar is not fitted because of the risk that is might jam and prevent use of the deck. The clear upper deck gives it some capability for carrying stores, and containerised troop accommodation could be added. The corvette would have simple defensive armament, two engine-

[10] Friedman *op cit* (n7) p138.

rooms and at least two zones, but nevertheless would not be operational after sustaining major damage.

The baseline corvette design offers a number of other advantages. As a small ship it could give young officers early experience of command. As a simple basic design, it would allow frequent design changes at low cost to test new technology and to help designers gain experience.

Very Long Range (VLR)

Since World War II, warships have relied on replenishment at sea to keep their fuel tanks, store rooms and magazines topped up. This is a demanding and expensive operation which takes the ship off station for a considerable time; there must therefore be a considerable advantage in giving escort ships sufficient fuel and stores for any mission without replenishment. In practice, 30 days at sea is likely to be the longest operational period.

Simple calculations show that this could be achieved with a 50 per cent increase in deep displacement. The increase in cost will be very much less; the increase in structural weight will be about 25 per cent which at £10,000 per tonne is not great. The ship will be larger and so increase the run of a few systems, but pipes and wires are not expensive; system costs rise when additional pumps and other equipment are needed. A slight decrease in speed for a larger ship may, however, have to be accepted if the cost of more powerful machinery is to be avoided.

Technically, it is simple to provide tanks for 30 days' fuel, though ballast will probably be needed, certainly in SWATH vessels. Provisions are also easy to stow, but it would not be possible to carry weapons for 30 days' fighting or sonobuoys for active search. In fact, the chance of any ship surviving many days of close combat is small. The transfer of missiles is possible today but it is slow and could not be carried out during an engagement; heavy usage would require a return to base. The biggest problem for the VLR ship might be expenditure of sonobuoys but VERTREP should be possible in this case.

There would be considerable overall savings in eliminating not only the AOR but also the need for its escorts. It should nevertheless be understood that these savings will not occur until a complete squadron of very long-range ships is in service. The savings

1 Towed array gear
2 EH 101
3 30mm gun

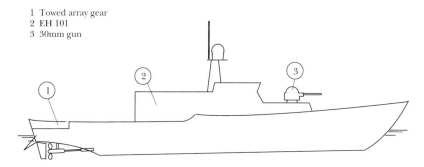

Figure 9/3: A sketch of a Very Long Range corvette with 30 days endurance without replenishment. The extra size makes room for a hangar.

are real but would occur well in the future: a fairly extreme 'spend to save' measure.

The very-long range ships, being bigger, will be better sea boats and will have other technical advantages. The corvette, at some 2200 tonnes, will be large enough to accommodate a hangar for its helicopter, and some of the savings from the abolition of the AOR can be used to give it basic maintenance facilities.

It is bound to be argued that a 2200-ton ship with one small gun and a helicopter is grossly under-armed, and there will be strong pressure to add more equipment. Similar criticism will be levelled at the VLR destroyer, which will grow to about 9000 tonnes. However, cost lies in equipment, not in steel, and will escalate rapidly if more weapons are fitted. In turn, with a limited budget, this will mean fewer ships.

SWATH

The case for the SWATH is put forward in Appendix 1 and in Chapter 5 and needs only to be summarised here. The SWATH offers a great reduction in vertical motions in return for a small increase in structural weight and cost. It may also require some additional systems for ballasting and for active fin stabilisation. The value of the increased operability given by this reduction in motions is hard to quantify.[11] In particular, there are limits on helicopter operation

[11] David K Brown 'The Value of Reducing Ship Motions' *Naval Engineer's Journal* ASNE (Washington, 1985).

A design study by Yarrow of a SWATH sonar ship for the MoD, quite similar to the corvettes discussed here.

imposed by wind speed, independent of motions[12], a limit usually ignored by the more enthusiastic advocates of the SWATH.[13] However, even a small increase in a ship's ability to operate its helicopters in rough weather is always valuable and may sometimes win a war.

The SWATH must operate at almost constant displacement and hence very long-range variants at least will require large ballast tanks for compensation as fuel is used. The SWATH configuration is convenient for helicopter operation and hence is should be possible to design a SWATH destroyer without a lift, saving some cost. However, the VLR destroyer will have a displacement of about 9000 tonnes and even a conventional ship of that size will only rarely be limited by bad weather. A decision on the destroyer can therefore be deferred until experience with the smaller SWATH corvette is

[12] Adrian R J M Lloyd & Peter J Hansom, *The Operational Effectiveness of the Shipborne Naval Helicopter* RINA Symposium, 'The Air Threat at Sea' (London, 1985).
[13] Colin Kennel & Brian White *Innovative Designs for North Atlantic Operations* Transactions SNAME (New York, 1985).

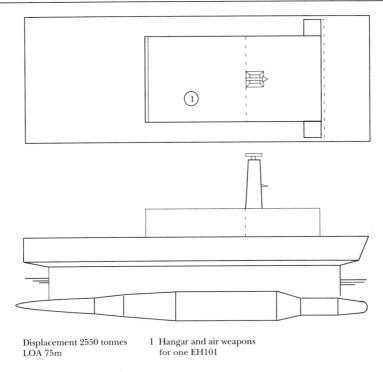

Displacement 2550 tonnes   1 Hangar and air weapons
LOA 75m   for one EH101

Figure 9/4: An outline of the SWATH corvette.

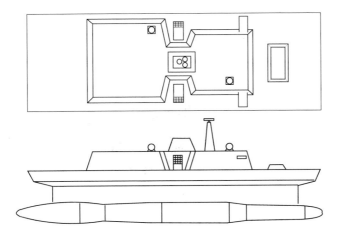

Figure 9/5 - and a SWATH destroyer. The configuration makes it easy to arrange the hangar, dispensing with lifts.

obtained. The benefits of reduced motion will be more significant in the smaller corvette, and the low-cost and uncomplicated corvette is an ideal choice for a prototype SWATH, likely to give a reliable and convincing demonstration of its advantages. In some roles the greater draft of the SWATH may be a drawback and it may be desirable to continue the building of a few monohulls.

Amphibious ships

In this discussion of amphibious ships the 'official' combination of two ASSs, two LPDs and six LSLs will be accepted and analysis confined to the problems of their design. The aviation support ship has already been discussed in the section dealing with cheap helicopter carriers.

The over-riding consideration is cost; if this is allowed to rise too far, the will of the government will inevitably weaken and any reinforcement is likely to rely exclusively on requisitioned vessels. The designer's problem is to produce the best vessel he can within a very tight budget.

A peculiarly British problem is that these ships will almost certainly be manned by merchant seamen of the Royal Fleet Auxiliary, since such men can be recruited more easily than RN ratings. The RFA men are more highly paid and have much more luxurious accommodation, but fewer men are needed. Though the RFA fleet is deregistered, it has been agreed that Department of Transport and international (IMO) safety rules and accommodation standards will still apply. If this is taken literally, lifeboats will still be needed in addition to landing craft and liferafts, making upper deck layout very difficult; the rules which forbid accommodation over fuel or ammunition stowage will also be difficult to meet.

Though this is not a legal requirement, there will also be strong pressure to connect machinery spaces, including the shaft tunnel, by low-level watertight doors, giving easy access between machinery spaces and helping operations with small crews. Such low-level doors represent a major hazard, however, in the event of damage. Vulnerability is a major problem; these ships are vital to the success of an operation and their loss or disablement could lead to the failure of the operation as well as to heavy casualties. Glib talk of building to 'merchant ships standards' overlooks the fact that these amphibious ships are not used as merchant ships; they are exposed to great risks, as shown in the Falklands war, when most of the LSLs were hit.[14]

Safety can never be absolute and cost must always be a consideration, but there is much that an experienced designer can do at low cost. It will not add greatly to the cost of the LPDs and ASSs to build to full warship standards of subdivision, though it would not be easy to achieve this in the LSLs. They should therefore at least reach SOLAS 90 passenger ship standards, which require a reasonable range of stability with two compartments flooded.

Since all ships carry a variety of inflammable and explosive stores, firefighting arrangements will need to be of high standard. It will require ingenuity to combine Merchant Navy regulations, warship practice and RFA training. There are excellent arguments for reducing signatures, improving shock resistance and adopting other warship features. Within a limited budget, limited improvements are possible, and should therefore be sought in these areas. Basic measures for signature reduction, for example, are relatively cheap and effective, and designers should therefore ensure that these are incorporated in the designs.

Armament is an even more vexed question. To be effective it will need quite comprehensive AIO and communications, which will be very expensive. The LPD and the ASS will require some such facilities in any case, as they will have to act as military headquarters in the early stages of any amphibious operation. In view of the Royal Navy's weakness in air defence for such an operation, every effort should be made to install Sea Wolf missile systems in the bigger ships. The LSLs may have to make do with light gun armament, provided mainly for the morale of their crews.

The LPDs pose no undue design problem and the *Fearless* is, in many ways, a good model. Diesel, or diesel-electric, propulsion will need a smaller crew than steam turbines and will probably be adopted. The concept of a 'through deck' LPD has many attractions (there can never be too many spare flight decks), but the accommodation of the antennae required for a headquarters ship on an island superstructure presents serious design difficulties. Great care will be needed before accepting a SLEP programme for the existing ships. They were built before modern corrosion protec-

---

[14] J D Brown, *The Royal Navy and the Falklands War* (London, 1987).

tion was introduced and many of their systems will need renewing. The full extent of the corrosion can only become apparent when the ships are opened up, and any apparent economy in life extension through SLEP may prove false.

The LSLs, on the other hand, present many design problems. The existing ships are already rather large for beaching and a farcical interpretation of merchant shipping regulations means that every beaching is treated as a 'grounding' which must be followed by a docking for inspection. In consequence, beaching is practised once, at most, during a commission. The smaller LCLs are much better beaching vessels, though rather small for open sea work. If beaching is a real requirement, smaller, lighter vessels will be needed and the design is unlikely to be compatible with passenger ship regulations. Modern cargo handling equipment with swivelling ramps, pallets and monorails can speed operations at low cost.[15]

The new force is more likely to use conventional LCUs than hovercraft (LCAC). Hovercraft have a much wider choice of beach than landing craft; studies suggest that they can use 70 per cent of the world's beaches, as against 15-20 per cent for conventional craft. Their high speed and ability to cross a beach and move inland is valuable, but mainly in the context of opposed landings where the transports might be a long way off shore. However, studies reported by Lewis and Band[16], suggest that the high cost of hovercraft is not justified if the bigger ships can close the coast. The hovercraft has great advantages for operations within the Norwegian fjords because of its high transit speed between the few beaches.

These purpose-built ships form the core of an amphibious expedition and will be supplemented by ships taken up from trade (STUFT), as they were in the Falklands. Conventional passenger liners built before 1990 can usually float with two compartments flooded but their freeboard may then only be 76mm, so that they are unlikely to float for long except in a dead calm.

Ro-Ro passenger ferries pose much greater hazards. If the vehicle deck is flooded they will capsize in seconds, as did *Herald of Free Enterprise* in 1986 off the Belgian coast. A recent report by the

---

[15] J C Dolton & P Silvia, *Concepts for a UK Replacement Amphibious Fleet* RINA Symposium 'Warship 86' (London, 1986).

[16] D R Lewis & E G U Band, *Air Cushion Craft for Amphibious Assault – The Next Generation* RINA Symposium 'Warship 86' (London, 1986).

Department of Transport recommended that nothing less than SOLAS 90 standards is even moderately safe in peacetime and that major alterations will be needed to virtually all existing ships to achieve that standard. Cargo Ro-Ro ships will capsize if even one big compartment is breached and should therefore never be used for transporting personnel or essential equipment.

Until the North Sea ferry fleet is brought up to SOLAS 90 standards there will be great risks in using these ships in the more hazardous conditions of war. Such risks may prove operationally necessary, but they must be minimised by dispersing troops and equipment over as many ships as possible. Safety is improved by running at light draught, and the temptation to overload may have fatal consequences. It must be repeated that the fire-fighting systems and even the very steel from which ferries are built are inadequate for war.

Mine countermeasure vessels

The designer of mine actuation systems can ring the changes on magnetic, acoustic, pressure and other signatures, perhaps selecting specific frequencies or characteristics of the desired target. To this he can add complications such as counters and time delay as used in World War II. An anti-MCMV mine is also quite feasible, and perhaps not in service only because of the relative ineffectiveness of MCM operations. Since it is easy to change the characteristics of a mine by reprogramming its microprocessor, it would seem that the MCMV and its equipment should also be versatile and adaptable. The need for low signatures is essential since hunting has only a moderate chance of locating a mine in a single pass on an average sea bed, with a corresponding chance of the MCMV passing over a mine and setting it off.

If the MCMV has to operate sweeps as well as to hunt, it will be about the same size as the Hunt class and, indeed, it will be hard to improve on that class. Most modern mines are unsweepable, but there are very large numbers of older mines in both the Soviet armoury and those of other counties. Sweeping is much quicker than hunting and it is unwise for any fleet to be without a sweeping capability; it is, however, virtually impossible to decide what proportion of MCM resouces should be devoted to sweeping. The ability to sweep deep anti-submarine mines (rising or Captor) is also

HMAS Rushcutter, a catamaran minehunter; note the container forming the operations room.

A wave piercing catamaran. A Vosper-Thornycroft study for a patrol boat similar to the holder of the Blue Ribband.

important, but all requirements can be met by unsophisticated craft such as the River class.

Hunters can be smaller, such as the *Sandown* class, though they may not be much cheaper. Versatility and adaptability can best be provided by a vessel with a broad upper deck and good stability, on to which new equipment can be fitted, possibly in containers or on pallets. This suggests a catamaran such as HMAS *Rushcutter* but the difficulty is that catamarans suffer from very high roll accelerations in rough seas. *Rushcutter* is intended for estuary use, where roll should not be a serious problem.[17]

The violence of rolling can be reduced by 'waisting' the hulls at the waterline but only to a limited extent, as it would be undesirable for an MCMV to be as sensitive to weight changes as a SWATH. Wave-piercing catamarans (see page 150) may be suitable but they, too, are probably weight sensitive and recent experience suggests that further work on seakeeping is needed. The effects of roll will be most sensitive at the deck edge (vertical acceleration) and high up (lateral acceleration) and so work areas should be arranged on the centreline and fairly low in the craft.

Mine warfare could occur worldwide and rapid deployment is not possible with the low transit speed of current MCMVs. Fast MCMVs are not impossible to build but speed would add greatly to their cost, reducing still further the numbers which could be made available. An alterative approach was suggested some years ago in a study of a vessel known as the 'Utility Minehunter'. In order to use resouces other than those involved in the Hunt class programme, it was proposed to produce large numbers of cheap and simple GRP hulls, with engines, AIO and sonar built into simple containers, dropped on to the hull and plugged in through a pre-cut wiring loom. The original scheme was for a catamaran, though a fairly conventional but very 'short-fat' monohull was adopted for production reasons. One possibility involved building many more cheap hulls than container sets and keeping them in critical locations. The containers could then be brought out in fast ships or even delivered by air.

One variant was to use electric propulsion driven by a battery which could be charged in safe water by a cheap and noisy diesel

---

[17] Brian L Robson, *Development of the RAN GRP Minehunter Design* Trans RINA (London, 1983).

A 'utility' minehunter with engines and equipment in containers dropped on to a very simple hull.

before entering a suspect area. Mine warfare is complicated and it would seem that effective MCM systems are likely to be too big to be deployed from helicopters or from the small, remote-controlled craft of the German Troika system.

Route surveillance

An alternative approach to mine countermeasures, outlined in Chapter 2, is to identify safe routes, clear of mines; actual disposal of mines is still an essential task but becomes a secondary one. The routes concerned, from Faslane to the open sea and the reinforcement routes across the Channel and North Sea, are quite lengthy and are widely separated. Routes on which the bottom is smooth and hard are important to ease the detection of mines, and choice of such routes will inevitably add to the mileage to be covered. Of course, there will remain areas where there is no easy path, and slow, conventional hunting will still have to be carried out.

With today's technology the only way of inspecting the seabed at speed is by using side-scan sonar towed behind a vehicle. Sets such as the AQS-14, used by USN Sea Stallion helicopters, give a clear picture at speeds of about 20 knots and, given precise navigation (difficult in a helicopter), the picture can be compared in a computer with a previous inspection to indicate any new and suspicious objects. Such contacts are marked using an acoustic transponder.

MCM *hovercraft*

Towing a sonar inevitably means that the vehicle reaches the mine before the sonar and so it is essential that it is virtually invulnerable to mines and, equally important, that it can hold a predetermined track with accuracy. The helicopter is vulnerable to acoustic mines, as was demonstrated off Haiphong, and is not easy to control accurately. Current helicopters can only tow a single sonar body which, with side scan, means that there is a gap in coverage under the body and that a very precise second run is needed to close the gaps.

Royal Navy trials have shown that the fully-skirted hovercraft satisfies the requirements of a sonar-towing vehicle very well. The cross-Channel SRN 4 can tow two sonars with overlapping beam patterns to ensure complete coverage and it has two pairs of airscrews which can be turned together or in opposition to give precise navigational control. Trials showed that an SRN 4 running at 10 knots could hold a set course over the bottom with a standard deviation of 4m

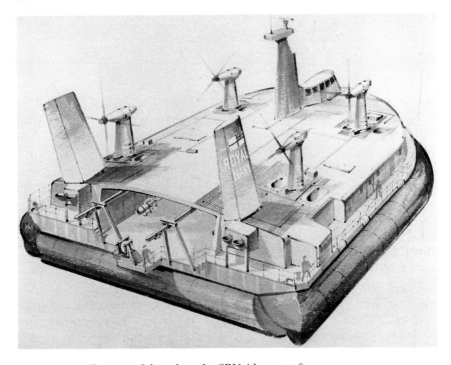

A route surveillance craft based on the SRN 4 hovercraft.

The BH 7 hovercraft as an experimental minehunter, with a sonar on a retractable strut abaft the mast.

in 2m waves and a 22-knot wind, a far better performance than any current MCMV.[18] The smaller BH7 craft with a single turnable screw and control 'puff ports' has good control under most conditions up to 2m seas and 20-knot winds.

The air cushion under the craft separates it from the sea, almost eliminating the need for shock protection and noise reduction of equipment. Trials with the older SRN 3 craft have also shown how resistant these craft are to explosions. The SRN 3 was moored to a buoy, hovering and unmanned, as seven full-size mines were exploded closer and closer to the craft, the last only just clear of the side. When that mine went off the craft disappeared in the spray plume but as it settled the craft was there, still hovering, with only minor damage to skirt and cabin from fragments of mine casing. The radio and radar, both standard commercial units, were still functioning. The crew would have been uninjured if secured in strong seats by lap straps. This was confirmed by later trials, at a lower level of shock, with a manned craft.

Other tests have shown that the standard commercial SRN 4 meets all noise signature requirements and has a very low pressure signature. In particular, the noise levels of a hovercraft do not increase much when turning, unlike those of a conventional ship, and a MCMV is turning for about 10 percent of the time during an

[18] David K Brown & Christopher M Plumb, *Hovercraft in Mine Countermeasures*, High Speed Surface Craft Conference (London, 1980).

A mine exploding close alongside the old SRN 3 hovercraft. It suffered very minor damage from splinters and was driven back with all equipment working.

operation. The magnetic signature would need attention, a simple and cheap change made by replacing some of the larger ferrous components.

Seakeeping has been discussed in Chapter 4 and it has been shown both by model tests in extreme seas and by the operation of small manned craft in very rough water that a hovercraft is safe in any weather. Disposal of mines, if necessary, is most economically carried out by less valuable craft, but if it needs to be done from the route surveillance hovercraft trials on BH7 have shown that the 193M hull-mounted sonar functions very well on a probe below the craft and there is no difficulty in operating mine disposal submersibles such as the PAP.

The hovercraft is basically a simple craft and can be built relatively cheaply. The SRN 4 is a first generation craft and, using production engineering techniques similar to those used in the more modern AP188 hovercraft, costs can be reduced further. More savings, compared with conventional craft, come because shock and noise mountings are not required and only limited attention is needed to magnetic signature. Since noise and signature isolation is inherent in the air cushion, frequent and expensive monitoring and rectification of signature levels is not needed.

Air-driven hovercraft are thirsty for fuel and the SRN 4s in service are a bad example because they use the Proteus engine, an early gas turbine. Even so, these craft, in an unmodified form would have an endurance of about 24 hours in the towed sonar role. More modern gas turbines, bigger propellers and other changes, together with overload fuel, could give an endurance in moderate wind and sea of at least 60 hours.

Commercial craft are very reliable; they work about 1500 hours per year, up to 14 hours per day at peak times and only about one percent of runs are aborted for mechanical problems. In an emergency they can be operated and maintained from any smooth beach.

The SRN 4 in its commercial form could be a good MCMV and priority should be given to purchasing sonar equipment which

An AP 188 hovercraft in Canadian Coastguard configuration. By clever production engineering and the use of standard components it is much cheaper than earlier craft.

could be installed on pallets so that these craft could be used in an emergency. If possible, one should be purchased or chartered as a development vehicle for more economical propulsion, further reduction of signatures and trials with better sonars. With a transit speed of 60-70 knots and a surveillance speed of about 20 knots, the hovercraft MCMV can cover much greater areas of the seabed than any other craft and all important performance attributes have been verified in full-scale trials.

It should be noted that the side wall craft (or SES), unlike a hover-craft, is not decoupled from the surface and though superior in shock and noise performance to a displacement vessel, it falls far short of that of a true hovercraft. MCM hovercraft do not have to be faster than the speed at which they can use their sonar but, since lightweight construction will be needed, the cost of providing more speed is reduced.

Location and, where necessary, disposal of camouflaged and buried mines is extremely difficult and with the collapse of the NATO Ermiss project there is no indication of a solution. It seems likely that a bottom crawling vehicle will be needed, probably remotely controlled from a mother ship. Any such system is likely to be very slow in operation, require large numbers and be very expensive.

10

Design and Build

A warship is the most complicated and expensive single artifact in the whole defence programme, and is built in small numbers. What makes a ship 'different' from any other item in the programme is that there is no prototype. The first of a class will only work if its development is backed by extensive modelling, both physical and in a computer; should the first ship not work, the subsequent vessels which will have been ordered before the first has been completed will not work either. The Government will be faced with a major financial disaster and the Navy will not receive the ships that it needs.

Shipbuilding and all the associated marine industries have been in decline for some 70 years and are not seen as offering attractive careers for bright young people, nor attractive returns for the money market. The Ministry's procurement policy must recognise that industry will not provide the talent nor the facilities required by the Navy without some form of government support; the chance of any significant contribution to research by the shipbuilding industry is remote indeed.

These problems are exacerbated by the increase in the time interval between designs,[1] as a result of which both Ministry and industry inevitably lack experience of warship design. Before World War II a destroyer would be at sea some 18 months after the time at which its design was begun, and in a three-year appointment a Constructor would span three classes. This speed of development allowed designers to learn their job, try new ideas and see the results in a short space of time. Today it takes eight to ten years to develop a ship from concept to trials. The subsequent lack of expe-

---

[1] David K Brown 'Defining a Warship', *Naval Engineer's Journal* ASNE (Washington, 1986).

rience is critical at both graduate and technician levels. This problem affects all NATO countries with the possible exception of France, which has maintained a single, strong team. The numerous new Soviet designs should provide their constructors with ample experience too.

This state of affairs is manifested in a failure to introduce new ideas, the waste of time and scarce effort in 're-inventing the wheel' and a much increased risk of error. Indeed there is a real doubt as to the continuing ability of the United Kingdom to muster one competent design team of the size needed for a frigate.[2] Attempts to introduce competition at the design stage leads to the farcical situation where the Ministry chooses between three mediocre designs rather than being able to pool the available talent to produce one good one.

In 1990, competition within the United Kingdom for building is still just possible and in recent years this style of procurement has been very successful in keeping costs down. However, there are some six yards with the capability to build frigates and the likely work programme is barely sufficient for one profitable yard. For GRP mine hunters, there are two or three possible builders (though only one with recent experience), but there is barely enough work for one. It is unlikely that there will be any effective competition for the next generation of ships unless uneconomic yards are kept open for social and political reasons.

There is no effective competition now for nuclear submarine construction. However, contacts specify a considerable amount of competition at sub-contract level, which amounts to a major part of the cost of a warship. Perhaps as important are the benefits which come from the learning curve. A steady throughput of similar products leads to a steady reduction in unit cost, and the effect of this can be considerable. For example, the last of the Hunt class built by Vosper Thornycroft required only half the man hours taken on the first.[3] Since there will therefore be no incentive for

---

[2] The size of a design team varies with the phase of the design. Initially, it may consist of four to six people, increasing to about forty as ideas firm up. In addition there will be many specialists involved, possibly part time, and there will be separate project teams on weapon systems and major items of machinery. By the time the building starts, there will be several hundred directly involved.

[3] Peter J Usher & John Dale, *Fibre Reinforced Plastics for Ship Construction – and other Applications* Offshore & Maritime Technology Transfer 86 Conference (London, 1986).

introducing innovative design on the part of the sole builder, it will have to come from the customer.

The relationship of the shipbuilder to the Ministry need not, and should not, be seen as that of a contractor supplying two to three thousand or more identical pieces of equipment to a customer. In the latter case it is possible for a number of prototypes to be built (thirty in the case of the Tornado), perhaps by more than one manufacturer, and these can be tried over the operational range and even tested to destruction. The successful version can then be built in numbers. This difference became very clear in the US 'Live Fire Testing' programme. Congress was concerned over the ability of US equipment, in all three services, to withstand the impact of enemy weapons and, quite sensibly, as they thought, directed that real, live weapons should be fired against representative equipment. They had not thought, of the implications for aircraft carriers and nuclear submarines.

No contractual conditions can cover the problems which could arise from the failure of the first of a class of warships. Shipbuilders are under-financed and could not be sued effectively for damages. As noted above, other ships of the class would be well advanced in construction by the time such a failure had been detected, and serious losses would fall on the Navy and the taxpayer.

Such situations are not uncommon in industry – big offshore installation and major chemical plants pose similar difficulties – but their solution is almost diametrically opposed to that preferred by the Ministry of Defence. The big oil companies recognise that the penalty of major failures in big projects inevitably falls on the customer and so run these big projects directly, appointing their own project managers to control contractors and their staff. Such major companies also recognise that in projects costing in excess of one hundred million pounds, it is not possible to specify every requirement in advance of contract, and that there must therefore be a considerable interaction between the customer and the contractor during both the design phase and the actual construction. The costs of changes during these phases are no doubt hotly debated, but the changes must be accepted by the contractor and the customer will have to pay if he is to have what he wants.

It is much easier for these large companies to carry out a full investment appraisal than it is for the Ministry. If a refinery is off-line because of late completion or teething troubles it is fairly simple to estimate the lost earnings; it is much more difficult to set a value on the loss of usage of a frigate. With rigid annual accounting there may even seem to be an advantage in delayed completion.

It should be possible to agree a notational value of a Frigate Day. It has been shown[4] that the cost of a frigate at sea for one day is about one hundred thousand pounds and, while cost and value are not equal, it must be assumed that value is, at least, not less than cost. Such a defined day value cannot be used as a contractual penalty on the builders for late delivery or for unreliability in service, as the limited capital backing of shipbuilders makes financial compensation impossible. Instead, this day value should be used by the Ministry in investment appraisal, weighing the cost of getting the ship built properly against a lower contract price which might lead to a ship which is late or needs much rectification afterwards. Such an appraisal would surely justify an adequately staffed and resourced project team in the Ministry with real, 'hands-on' control over the contractor and sufficient professional overseers on site.

Industry has much to offer, and the aim must be a partnership between the Ministry and the shipbuilders from which both benefit. The builders' special skills lie in the area of production engineering, from which they can only derive benefit under a fixed price contract, set by competition. Since it is inevitable that competition will wither away, procedures must be devised by which the builder receives a generous share of the profits from improved productivity.

The profitability of warship building has, in the past, been linked with export business. Such business is small and likely to decline further. Any country which can afford a modern frigate is likely to have most of the industrial capacity to build such a vessel itself, though most countries lack research and development ability, design skills and the capability to make the more advanced equipment. It should still be possible for the United Kingdom to sell design agency services based on British research and on remaining British design skills. Such designs are more likely to use British equipment, this benefitting specialist British defence manufacturers also.

---

[4] David J Andrews & David K Brown *Cheap Warships are not Simple* SNAME Symposium 'Ship Costs and Energy' (New York, 1987).

Design

Design is an emotive word, used with many meanings. One of the better definitions of engineering design is that given by the Fielden Committee in 1963: 'Engineering design is the use of scientific principles, technical information, and imagination in the definition of a structure, machine or system to perform specified functions with the maximum economy and efficiency.'

Today, 25 years later, we would add safety and care for people and the environment but perhaps Fielden saw these as part of the 'specified functions'. Design is not the production of working drawings, though production engineering is an important aspect of Fielden's 'maximum economy' and design is also not merely an artistic style, though aesthetics should play an important part in warship design.

Design should begin with a clear statement of the function of the ship. It is sometimes suggested, not entirely without justice, that warships are rarely used in war for the role for which they are designed and hence there is no need to specify a function at the design stage. This is not a strong argument. The ship should be designed for the tasks perceived at the time and with sufficient flexibility to make it adaptable for new roles.

The present system of Staff Targets and Staff Requirements (Sea) seems wrong in that such a system presupposes a solution at too early a stage. The Defence Staff should first issue policy papers setting out the tasks which it is envisaged will fall to the navy in years to come. Such policy papers are produced today and are generally satisfactory. From these papers should come a functional statement of the operational role of a new class of ship together with guidance on the resources likely to be available. This will usually be in the form of a provisional cash limit but other constraints, such a manpower, can also be given. Even so, there may be little choice for major weapon systems.

The next stage, the present Staff Requirement, should be replaced by a 'Controllerate solution', led by the Technical Departments, offering a number of viable alternatives which meet the operational, technical and economic requirements (or, more realistically, offering compromises which fail to some degree in achieving all that is asked for). During this phase there will be frequent need for consultations with all the various departments of the Ministry – research, operational, financial and manning – as well as between the various specialised technical departments. These interactions will be handled by a Design Co-ordination Group. In the past, there have been problems because departmental representatives have not been given the authority to act as full delegates. In consequence, decisions agreed in the group are challenged later by Department whose representatives in the Group had agreed to them earlier.

The size and complexity of a warship is such that the set of design interactions is far larger than in any other item of equipment and, because of its complexity, this stage can only be handled within the Ministry. It has already been suggested that the United Kingdom can now muster only one warship design team and also that expertise in production engineering lies with the builders. The solution begins to be apparent: what is required is a single core of professional engineers of all specialisations, kept together, gaining experience, round which can be built the larger team needed to see the design through to construction.

The leader of the team should be the Ship Designer, who can employ all techniques of management to achieve a timely and economic output. Since ship design is the *raison d'être* of the naval architect, it follows that ship design teams must be led by a naval architect. This simple fact has been eroded by talk of equal opportunities for other professions and by misinformed advocates of systems engineering (a very useful tool frequently used by the naval architect). In all the present debate on the styles of buildings on land, no one suggests that anyone but an architect should design them.

This argument leads to giving renewed authority for the Royal Corps of Naval Constructors, set up following a paper by William White, using much the same arguments a those outlined above.[5] More recently, the US Department of Defense, disillusioned by the high cost of 'total package procurement', used much the same approach for the *Arleigh Burke* (DDG 51) design, apparently with very satisfactory results. A small body of government designers was strengthened by people from industry who worked together on the design before competitive tendering for building was sought. It seems that the T-AGOS SWATH design was carried out in much the same way with equally good results.

---

[5] David K Brown, *A Century of Naval Construction* (London, 1983).

It is probably not necessary for this Corps to handle weapons design as in that area there are prototypes to be tested and approved; there is sufficient talent in industry and the firms are generally well financed. There is, however, need for the Corps to be informed customers for weapons and also to have more direct authority over weapon installation.

Research and development

To ensure that future warships are economic, durable, reliable and fit for their intended purpose it is essential that design skills are firmly rooted in well directed and well validated research and development (R & D), and that there is access to deep expertise in the research establishments. This was recognised in the 1840s when the Admiralty Chemist's Department[6] was set up, in 1872 when the Director of Naval Construction (DNC) sponsored William Froude in setting up the world's first ship model tank at Torquay (which went on to win international fame as the Admiralty Experiment Works), and when a later DNC created the Naval Construction Research Establishment[7], against strong opposition, to carry out research into both structural design and resistance to explosions. In much the same way the Admiralty Engineering Laboratory[8] was set up at West Drayton for engineering R & D and the Admiralty Material Laboratory for material studies.

Such tasks are as vital to the Navy of today as when these establishments were created and new problems, such as signature reduction and high-speed manoeuvring of submarines, have arisen. Unfortunately, a perverse doctrine has grown up which holds that research is indivisible. This leads to meaningless debate as to whether structural design is more or less important than electronic countermeasures. Both, of course, are needed, and it is virtually impossible to divide limited resources on this basis. Given the Navy's current task of maintaining a force of forty frigates, it is quite clear that a structural research establishment is needed; there will still be difficult problems in allocating money between building and future seed corn, but no one will argue, as they do now, that

---

[6] David K Brown, *Before the Ironclad* (London, 1990).
[7] M M Postan, D Hay and J D Scott, *Design and Development of Weapons* (London, 1965).
[8] Brown *op cit* (n5).

structural work should be stopped. The design team must control most of the research programme directly, though they must still leave the research team some scope to freelance.[9]

A similar fallacy is that defence takes too much of the country's R & D resources; again the implication is that R & D is finite and indivisible. A high-technology company would expect to spend at least 10 percent of its turnover on research and, allowing for differences in defining research, the Ministry's 11.7 percent is certainly not too high. It is industry itself which has failed , for a variety of reasons, to invest enough in R & D.

Ships are big, and so are the facilities needed for their R & D. The existing establishments have unique and very expensive facilities, which exist nowhere else in the United Kingdom and only rarely in the other NATO countries. More important, they have exceptional expertise, not yet entirely destroyed, over a wide range of subjects. There is no way in which the remaining shipbuilding industry can support this work as the industry has virtually no work other than that for the Ministry, and competitive tendering prevents them from adding to their overheads. The facilities must be owned by the Ministry and controlled directly by the designers.

The design team should be as small as possible to do the job, and must rely on specialist groups when difficult problems arise. These groups, specialising in stability, materials, signature reduction, gearing, structures, weapon integration and hydrodynamics to name a few, will have more specialist expertise than can reasonably be included within the design project, and will also have the ability to make informed use of the research establishments or contractors as appropriate for problems beyond their own skills. It is upon these specialist groups, who also write the specifications, audit the design and certify safety, that the design team relies. Only the Ministry can provide the continuity of expertise needed and today even that is at risk.

The engineering dimension

During World War I the DNC, Sir Eustace Tennyson d'Eyncourt,

---

[9] As a rough guide, it is often said that 90 percent of research should be programmed and that research workers should follow their hunches for the other 10 percent. Of course, much of the planned 90 percent will have originated within the research area.

pointed out that the Navy was the largest engineering organisation in the county and yet had no engineer on the Board. His draft letter to the Prime Minister noted that 'design and the carrying out of design into practice is all important, and continued, 'in order to carry weight, I should have a seat on the Board and should then be of more use to the country'. D'Eyncourt did at least have the title of Principal Technical Adviser to the Board of Admiralty, which had quite considerable moral authority[10].

Today, there is no post of Chief Engineer to the Ministry of Defence nor is there a Chief Engineer in the Controller of the Navy's department. There is a Chief Scientist and occasionally he may have an engineering background. The Navy needs a Chief Scientist but it also needs a Chief Engineer who has spent his career in design. The career of a scientist and of a designer are very different and no one can give the right input at the highest level in both areas. The lack of the Chief Engineer is felt most when decisions have to be made on which project is to be selected for production. It is unlikely that a qualified design engineer would have allowed the mismatch of requirements and cost involved in the Nimrod AEW aircraft to go forward.

NATO *technical collaboration and design*

It seems obvious that sharing the work of design and construction between several countries will economise on the use of scarce resources. In practice, the expected benefits do not seem to materialise; the Royal Air Force has estimated the cost of their share of the joint Tornado programme was greater than it would have cost as a national programme (though it has been suggested that had the Tornado been a UK national programme is would undoubtedly have been cancelled on the grounds of cost).

On a much smaller scale, I was involved in the NATO ERMISS programme, involving five countries.[11] There was a project office in Koblenz, West Germany, with a project engineer from each participant responsible for placing contacts for research and building a

---

[10] Brown, *op cit* (n5).

[11] H W Groning, 'A New Concept in Mine Counter Measures' *International Defence Review* (London, 1984).

NFR 90 – the ill fated NATO frigate. It failed because its weapons programme was out of phase with the ship, costs rose as the designers tried to please everyone, and the design process itself was too slow.

test section. Had this been a UK project, it is unlikely that this task would have provided sufficient work for one man, let alone five. There were also frequent references made to headquarters and six-monthly steering committee meetings. The main problem in the project management was reaching agreement on work sharing. The agreed objectives were necessarily conflicting, requiring the project office to share the work equally while at the same time seeking the most cost-effective solution. It was not easy to find a compromise.

A further and more serious problem is that approval from each participating government will be for one stage only, and all work will have to stop while the next stage is negotiated (which may take a year or more. A UK national frigate design can take 8 to 10 years from conception to acceptance; the NFR 90 would have taken at least 15 years and probably even 20 years.

Another reason for the failure of the NFR 90 was the problem of designing a ship to accept weapons which were not in existence. This is a certain recipe for failure and in this particular case not all the participants even wanted the same weapon fit. The organisation for this aspect of the project was moreover unfamiliar to all concerned, and quite unsatisfactory. There was a project office, with representatives from each county responsible to the Director, but with each also responsible for seeing that his own country's requirements were met. This office was responsible for organising a consortium of many firms from all participating countries, many of whom were not keen on sharing trade secrets. Several participating countries were more familiar with carrying out preliminary 'concept' design in-house and there was little experience in industry for this phase of the work. It is probably not unkind to suggest that industry expected failure in these circumstances and did not deploy the best available resources.

Even bi-lateral programmes do not have a high rate of success. The Netherlands Standard frigate has little in common with the German Type 122 and attempts to design the Type 22 as an Anglo-Dutch project failed because of the problems associated with work sharing. It was clear that the main machinery would be Olympus-Tyne COGOG, while for equal shares of the work the Dutch would have provided all auxiliary machinery. For the UK government, this would have meant supporting Rolls Royce to the detriment of every other marine engineering company, and this was not acceptable. There was also a problem over the length of the ship as determined by the available drydocks in the two countries. An attempt to combine the Type 23 and M class failed at the start. The 'Tri-partite' programme involving France, Belgium and the Netherlands has produced some good MCMVs but the partners do not seem keen to repeat the process for the next generation.

One good thing which has emerged from the NFR 90 programme was the realisation that engineering standards, such as NES and MILSPEC, in the participating countries differed little in principle. A common set of the major standards was agreed, which could make any future collaboration much easier. It seems strange that NATO does not have a standard Memorandum of Understanding setting out the administrative basis for all projects.

A tiny project with some features which could be used more widely on bigger schemes is the US/Canada/UK research into GRP superstructures. The emphasis is on each county contributing the aspects which it does well rather than sharing every aspect equally. The project grew out of separate national programmes and has cut out a lot of duplication and has benefitted from the different approaches. In particular, it was agreed that the end product would not be a research report, gathering dust, but a specification, valid in all three countries, for building GRP superstructures.

The very real difficulties of collaboration should not be allowed to obstruct the advantages of sharing ideas and talent. It is unlikely that several countries will agree precisely on the requirements for a warship, and hence a collaborative ship is probably best as a modular design (see Chapter 4), easing (though not eliminating), the problems. The design team should be an integrated Ministry/industry team, led by the Ministry rather than a project office divided between 'them and us'. The US *Arleigh Burke* design would provide a good starting point for such an organisation.

Research and Development seems a promising area for effective collaboration. NATO could have a single establishment for, for example, structures research. The facilities would be jointly owned and some work would be multi-national. In addition, there could be national teams working on specific tasks, hiring time on the facilities.

For design projects it will be necessary for Government approval to cover a one stage and a year so that work is not interrupted while approval is obtained for the next stage. Even so, there will still be more formal procedures than in a national design and more need for consultation, thereby inevitably increasing the total time for completion. It will therefore be wise to start with a highly innovative design; for if it is conventional at the start, it will almost certainly be obsolete by the time it is completed, though the NATO Hydrofoil programme, whose sole output was the USN PHM *Pegasus*, is not encouraging. It was largely for this reason that Constructors from all the NATO frigate countries believed that NFR 90 should have been a SWATH.

Most countries in NATO – and the Soviet Union – have a Corps of Constructors based on the eighteenth century French *Genie Maritime*, and even in the United States supporters of the Construction Corps have not died. Such a common heritage should enable a real partnership to be formed though there is little sign of it happening. Perhaps the answer is a NATO (or European) *Genie Maritime*.

Decisions

In a parliamentary democracy, major decisions on design and building must involve approval by committees representing the three services, financial departments and ministers. There seems little wrong in principle with the present procedures but a good

Earlier decision-making was much simpler and quicker, and was right at least as often as decisions by modern methods.

deal wrong in the way they are used. Bryson[12] has given a good summary of the procedures as they then were. Today, all stages are approved by the Equipment Policy Committee, chaired by the Chief Scientist, with tri-service and finance representation.

In the early stages they will attempt to compare the effectiveness of alternative solutions such as patrol aircraft, frigates and SSNs in anti-submarine warfare. If a frigate is selected, they will debate the merits of different options in the next stage. The overall cost of the programme will be matched against available resources. Finally, before the order, ministers will consider social factors such as the need to relieve unemployment in special areas.

The first problem is that senior officers in some departments are not kept in touch with discussions at lower levels. As Head of Concept Design I was given a very full briefing at the start by the Director General Ships and after each meeting of the group had to report back. Sometimes the arguments of other departments were sound and acceptable and the design was modified; if they were not acceptable, the issue would be taken up at higher level and resolved

[12] Sir Lindsay Bryson *The Procurement of a Warship* Transactions RINA (London, 1984).

quickly. As a result, the Director General was not taken by surprise by the proposed solution in the final paper, had agreed most points in advance and had a clear view of both sides of the argument where there were still unresolved points. In some other departments junior officers came to the group meetings with no idea about what their senior officers wanted and, in consequence, these senior officers were taken by surprise when the submission on the design reached them.

In any committee allocating scarce resources some two thirds of the members will be opposed to any project put before them. Even in an all-Naval committee members will feel that they could spend the money better on a submarine, aircraft or some other equipment rather than the frigate which they are discussing. Clearly, this clash of interests is greater in a tri-service committee. This problem is exacerbated because the opposing members will not have been involved in the lower level discussions and will have had little time to read the paper and understand the proposal. They will rely on their Staff to brief them. Staff Officers, being bright, ambitious officers, will want to appear clever to their masters and it is much easier to appear clever in destructive criticism than in supporting a proposal.

This attitude leads to the proposer making his paper longer and longer in a vain attempt to pre-empt such criticism. In practice, the more detail there is in the paper, the easier it is to criticise. In contrast, there is in the library aboard HMS *Belfast* a copy of the submission to the prewar Board of Admiralty seeking approval to place a contract for her building. The paper itself is half a side in length and is accompanied by an appendix describing the ship on another four sides together with a standard form giving two sheets of statistics on the ship. The short paper concludes, 'In anticipation of approval, the drawings have been sent to the shipbuilders'. Formal approval was given two weeks later.

Decision making depends on proper authority being delegated together with a full dialogue between the delegate and his master. High level meetings can then concentrate on a very few major issues.

There have been too many inquiries leading to reorganisations of the design departments. This is not where the problem lies; the failings lie in setting realistic targets and requirements and keeping them unchanged. It is a problem which has been well described:

'There is no such thing as a bad design, only bad Staff Requirements'.[13]

The Staff must concentrate on a better definition of the roles of the new ship though both the Chief Designer and Chief Scientist can make useful contributions. The development of the design is the task of the Chief Designer though, of course, he must carry the Staff, his customer, with him in all major decisions. Informed delegation should enable most decisions to be agreed at an early stage, and left unchanged, so that the high level approval will cause no surprises and early agreement.

[13] This observation was made, and frequently repeated, by Anthony Preston.

11

Conclusions

Those who may have thought that the end of the threat from the Warsaw Pact would lead to eternal peace have had to think again following Iraq's attack on Kuwait. However, Britain and Western Europe remain most at risk on the Atlantic trade routes since defeat there could be total and even late in 1990 there is no reduction in the rate at which the Soviet Navy is building submarines. Despite this, the reduction in superpower tension is bound to lead to corresponding reductions in defence budgets, exacerbating the conflicts between resources and commitments and between quality and quantity.

There can be no perfect solution to such problems but I hope that the ideas put forward in this book will contribute to the debate on ways of easing them. The central theme is the intelligent use of innovative technology which at the same time is well proven and this depends upon substantial investment in research and development largely, but not entirely, under the control of the designer. Advanced technology should be applied at all levels; a transom flap may only offer small benefits in most classes but its cost is even smaller and if enough small improvements are made the overall benefit in effectiveness and economy can be large. The designer must get it all right, even the details.

It is certain that the cost of a frigate will continue to rise with the inevitable and necessary increases in capability. The next class for the Royal Navy will almost certainly be an AAW ship, a Type 42 replacement and, as such, it will be more expensive than a Type 23. With rising unit costs it will be difficult to maintain even forty up-to-date ships.

The Royal Navy is weak in air power and air defence, lacking true carriers. The new generation of fighters have a short take-off and the possibility of an affordable small carrier and its aircraft needs re-examination though, as discussed, the problems are formidable.

Some form of HILO mix, for all the political risk pointed out be the House of Commons Defence Committee, seems desirable, particularly if combined with an increase in the number of big helicopters at sea. The Very Long Range ships should led to savings in the AOR and its escorts and make more ships and aircraft available in the front line. They are needed to protect merchant ships, or more exactly, cargoes, and not sea lanes.

The Atlantic is a stormy ocean and the well proven seakeeping of the SWATH gives such vessels a clear advantage. A squadron of SWATH corvettes, with towed array, should be built to demonstrate and evaluate the operational advantages of such ships and also to show that the price is not excessive.

The fleet exists so that the United Kingdom can use the sea to her advantage and deny its use to her enemies. The principal user is, or should be, the British Merchant Navy and it must be a matter of deep concern that of the fifteen ships chartered to take the 7th Armoured Brigade to Kuwait only one was British registered. It is also worrying that most of these ships were Ro-Ro vessels, pre SOLAS 90, whose hazards have been so tragically demonstrated not only by *Herald of Free Enterprise* but also by the fire in the *Scandinavian Star*. A strong merchant fleet is as important as the Royal Navy to the United Kingdom.

When resources are scarce it is essential that proper use is made of what is available. Much more attention should be given to investment appraisal, weighing future benefits or savings against first cost. Such a balance is not easy to draw, particularly as over-optimistic estimates of future benefits are often made in a deliberate attempt to justify increased current spending. The design organisation should have considerable delegated authority to make decisions in this aspect.

Ships really are different. They are complex, individually expensive and built without a prototype; there is no justification whatsoever for forcing their procurement to follow an identical pattern to that for aircraft and tanks, built in large numbers after exhaustive trials of many prototypes. Design skills and experience are scarce and diminishing in all professions and at all grades, making a nonsense of competition in design. The spur of competition is there for the design team in doing better than the opposition, or even allies, within the limits of resources available.

Good design is the key to value for money and the user is often the last to recognise the need for change. In 1958 I bought my first new car, a Morris Minor 1000, still regarded as a classic. I was delighted with it but the designer, Alex Issigonis, was already far advanced with a vastly superior car, the Mini. The difference was mainly in the way the components were arranged, giving more space and superior performance in a smaller package. The problems and opportunities of the warship designer are very similar.

A single design team could exist either within government service or a government owned agency; both have advantages and matching disadvantages. In an evenly balanced situation there is much to be said for leaving well alone: the record of the Ship Department of the Ministry of Defence in completing warships on time and to cost is good[1] and one should build on success. I am proud of my membership of the Royal Corps of Naval Constructors and I believe that a central design team should be based on this Corps.[2]

Innovative design is the only way to make effective use of limited funds.

Finally, I have always believed in the need 'to stir the pot with vigour' and hope that the ideas put forward here will indeed provoke a vigorous discussion.

---

[1] David K Brown *A Century of Naval Construction* (London, 1983).
[2] The senior naval architects of three of the largest warship builders are members of the RCNC.

Appendix 1

SWATH

SWATH stands for Small Waterplane Area, Twin Hull. Such vessels have two deeply submerged cylindrical hulls connected by narrow struts to a platform well above the water surface. The submerged hulls are little affected by most waves which leave the platform level, dry and undisturbed. In the most severe seas, the SWATH will follow the wave surface with motions still much less vigourous than those of a conventional ship.

In waves, the SWATH will be able to maintain speed better than a conventional ship and because it is much steadier, it is able to operate sensors, weapons and helicopters when other vessels cannot. The resulting gain in operational capability is marked (see Chapter 4, Seakeeping) and has been proven in trials with sea-going SWATHs of up to 4500 tonnes. The US experimental SWATH, *Kaimolino*, of

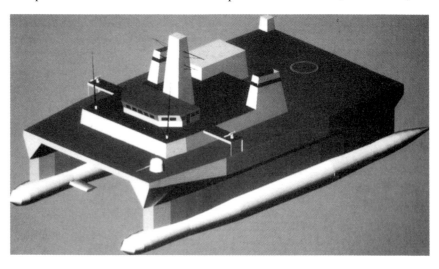

A conceptual SWATH by YARD.

only 200 tonnes, has shown seakeeping comparable with that of a 2500-tonne monohull sailing in company. Technically, SWATH is a well-proven concept.

There are a number of problems with SWATH and, though none is very serious, they have to be borne in mind before deciding on such a concept. In this world benefits are rarely free.

A SWATH hull will be heavier than a monohull carrying the same payload by some 10-15 percent and correspondingly more costly. Note that these increases are on the hull cost and weight and not on the overall figures as is sometimes implied. The underwater surface area of the SWATH will be about 60 percent greater, adding to drag and making fuel consumption worse. Comparisons are not easy because, though a SWATH will be more expensive than a monohull carrying the same payload, it will be very considerably smaller

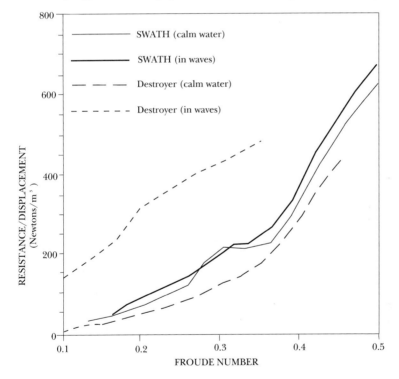

Appendix Figure 1: A comparison of the power required by a SWATH and a conventional destroyer of the same displacement in calm water and in waves. While the destroyer requires least power in calm water, it requires vastly more in waves than the SWATH, which is relatively unaffected by the sea.

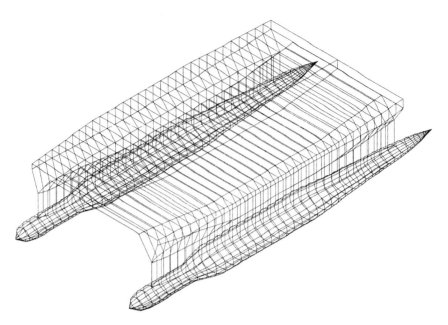

Appendix Figure 2: A computer representation of the lines of a 2000-tonne SWATH.

and cheaper than a monohull offering the same seakeeping capability (see Chapter 5).

The machinery arrangement will not be easy; either the prime movers will be placed in the submerged hulls, with long and complex uptake and downtake ducting, or, if the engines are in the platform, there will be difficulties in transmission. Electric drive seems the most promising arrangement for frigate-sized vessels.

SWATHs have long periods of pitch and heave which account for their small amplitude motions in most seas, but they respond to waves with a long period of encounter such as those overtaking slowly from astern. To damp out motions in following seas, it will be essential to fit stabilising fins forward and aft on the hulls and the after ones, at least, will need active control.

If the weight of a SWATH changes, it will lead to a much greater change of draught than such a weight change would cause in a conventional ship. Four tonnes off a 2000-tonne SWATH will raise the craft one centimetre. As fuel is used, corresponding ballast will be needed and, as in submarines, margins for future additions will have to be in the form of solid ballast which can be removed as the new items are fitted. The design of a SWATH involves many more variables than a monohull and a bigger design team will be needed and more preliminary modelling, both physical and mathematical, will be necessary.

If improved operational capability in rough weather is needed, as it would seem to be in the North Atlantic, SWATH should prove the cheapest and best solution. In war, the ability to operate helicopters in severe sea states may be the deciding factor.

---

[1] Further information about SWATH vessels can be found in:

Jerry L Gore 'SWATH ships' *Naval Engineers' Journal* (Washington, February 1985).

C G Kennel, B White, E N Comstock 'Innovative Designs for North Atlantic Operations' Transactions SNAME (New York, November 1985).

Proceedings of the RINA SWATH symposia.

Appendix 2

Reinforcement Convoys

For some 45 years the principal threat to Western Europe has usually been seen as an attack by the Soviet Army across the European plains. Recent political changes have made such an assault much less likely since even a maverick Soviet government would no longer have the support of its former Warsaw pact allies and would also have a start line much further east. However, a land war cannot be entirely ruled out and, should one break out, very considerable reinforcement will be needed from the United States and, to a lesser extent, from the United Kingdom. In either case, heavy equipment must go by sea, as illustrated by the recent US Army deployment to Saudi Arabia. To some extent, men can be flown in and can use pre-positioned equipment. However, big dumps of equipment are very vulnerable to attack, probably more so than a convoy of ships at sea.

A recent House of Commons Defence Committee report has given some indication of the scale of reinforcement which would be required and some of the key points are worth summarising. In the first 30 days, 800 ship lifts would be needed from the United States and only 200 of these could be supplied by the United States; Europe would have to find the rest. As a back up, between 1000 and 2500 ship lifts per month would be needed; 800 of these consisting of military equipment, 1500 economic supplies. Even without serious losses, such a rate of supply would require about 5000 merchant ships.

One US armoured division requires 100,000 tonnes of cargo of which 40 percent will not fit into containers. This division will then need 1000 tonnes of supplies each day it is in action, mainly petrol, oil and lubricant.

US plans call for six divisions to arrive in 14 days followed by a further fourteen divisions and twenty-one brigade groups as back up. Britain plans to ship 125,000 troops and 21,000 vehicles across the Channel and North Sea and return 120,000 families to the United Kingdom. This is well within the capacity of the existing ferry services if they are not attacked.

In a major land war involving NATO, the European navies would be fully supported by the United States Navy. However, in the first 14 days or so, the Royal Navy would provide most of the escorts in the Eastern Atlantic. The continuing fall in the number of merchant ships registered in the United Kingdom and Western Europe must be of great concern, and the shortage was emphasised by the difficulty in finding ships to transport a much smaller force to the Gulf.

Appendix 3

Blockade at Sea

Twice this century, the United Kingdom has been close to defeat as a result of the destruction of merchant ships by submarines. In the first quarter of 1917 the average *daily* rate of sinking was ten ships of some 23,500 gross tons. This rate of loss was far in excess of the building rate and with the lack of stored food and the relatively inefficient farming methods of the day starvation was a genuine prospect.

The position in World War II is less clear cut. The climax of the Battle of the Atlantic came with the great convoy battles of spring 1943. The position appeared bleak; in March 1943, 120 ships of 693,000 gross tons were sunk which, added to the 7,750,000 tons sunk in 1942, seemed a prelude to imminent disaster. Churchill's much quoted comment, 'The only thing which ever really frightened me during the war was the U-Boat peril' probably refers to this period. However, reconsideration of the facts suggests that the war in the Atlantic had been a more dangerous threat in earlier years of the war and that the battle had largely been won by 1943. Anti-submarine measures had been increasing in effectiveness and when the U-Boats re-deployed in large numbers they were sunk in correspondingly large numbers.

Even more important, the massive shipbuilding programme in the United States was delivering merchant ships at about 1,000,000 tons per month from October 1942, which was far in excess of the sinkings. On this basis, the worst time was in late 1940, with losses at about 500,000 tons per month offset only by about 100,000 tons of new construction. British agriculture was much more productive than in 1917 and actual starvation less likely.

It seems from German documents[1] that Dönitz was beginning to

---

[1] J P M Showell *U Boat Command* (London, 1989).

lose faith in victory in the Atlantic by about summer 1942. Though defeat of the Allies in the Atlantic was unlikely once the American building programme was rolling, not only of merchant ships but of their escorts too, shortage of shipping imposed serious limitations on military operations at least until 1944.

The threat today

Should the political turmoil in the Soviet Union throw up a maverick dictator bent on military action against the West he would have the capability to impose an Atlantic blockade. With the virtual collapse of the Warsaw Pact, Soviet troops have lost their allies and are geographically far removed from Western Europe. It might seem attractive to use the Soviet Navy rather than launch the land armies across Europe. Such a naval blockade could be aimed at Europe with much less risk of US intervention than an attack on land and, conceivably, the Soviets could impose their will without the problems and dangers of occupation.

The capability of the Soviet Navy to attack and destroy merchant shipping in the North Atlantic is formidable. The Northern fleet alone has about 50 SSNs, 32 SSBNs and 32 SSKs, all far more capable than the U-boats of 1943, together with 115 strike aircraft. Even if the more modern SSNs were held back in defence against intervention by the US Strike Fleet, there would be enough of the older boats to interrupt the Atlantic supply routes. Such a capability must be seen, at least, as a potential threat which, coupled with an unstable leadership, could easily and quickly become direct.

The recent events in the Gulf have made people aware of the dangers to the West of an interruption to oil supplies and have also shown a new enemy whose power was little appreciated.

Europe's vital supplies

Europe is critically dependant on oil supplies and the following tables show the peace-time demand in Europe, and the sources. It has not proved possible to assemble complete and consistent data for this appendix and the figures given should be taken as general indications rather than precise figures for today. The data refer to different years and it would seem that the definition used varies though these differences are not large enough to affect the thrust of the argument. The fact that such data are not readily and quickly available is yet another indication that the threat of the maritime blockade is not taken seriously; the figures which are given show how serious the threat could be.

TABLE 1: EUROPEAN OIL CONSUMPTION (1985)[2]
(million tonnes)

Germany	114
France	84
Italy	83
United Kingdom	78
TOTAL (Western Europe)	569

TABLE 2: EUROPEAN OIL SUPPLIES (million tonnes)

Imports		
	Crude	312
	Products	101
Local Supplies		
	UK & Norway	194

TABLE 3: SOURCES OF IMPORTS (million tonnes)

USSR, by pipeline	89
USA	11
Latin America	43
North Africa	82
West Africa	48
Middle East	152

Note: Of these imports, 120 million tonnes come through Suez, a further 25 million through the Eastern Mediterranean and 5 million round the Cape of Good Hope.

[2] *Know More About Oil – World Statistics* Institute of Petroleum (1986).

In a conflict with the Soviet Union, the 89 million tonnes through her pipeline would obviously stop, while the 194 million from the North Sea would be very vulnerable. Clearly, protection of these offshore installations should be given high priority though this would not be easy. Even in peacetime, Western Europe needs over 400 million tonnes of oil by sea. These oil supplies are also vulnerable at source, mainly in the Middle East, and in transit, particularly at Suez and in the Mediterranean.

The European Community can feed itself, to a considerable extent due to the much derided Common Agriculture Policy. Diet might be unbalanced and far from interesting but at least one good harvest can be relied on. This productive agriculture is, however, critically dependent on the supply of fertilisers by sea, mainly as phosphate rock. About 19 million tonnes are needed annually, of which more than half comes from Morocco and most of the rest from the United States. The table below lists a few other major imports to Western Europe in 1985.

TABLE 4: OTHER IMPORTS (million tonnes)	
Dry bulk	238.0
Iron ore	110.0
Coal	73.0
Grain	24.0
Bauxite and Aluminium	16.0
Manganese	0.9
Zinc	0.4
Sulphur	1.0

Interruption of these supplies would be damaging but the impact would be less immediate than that from loss of oil supplies.

The United Kingdom is in a rather better position than countries in the rest of Europe. Oil imports of some 50 million tonnes are more than offset by exports of 95 million. Phosphate fertiliser is probably the most critical, followed by metallic ores.

Shipping

The supply of at least 400 million tonnes of oil needs a lot of shipping. For many years there has been a world surplus of tankers but this has been much reduced by old age, by inducements to scrap and by losses in the Iran-Iraq war (mainly ships damaged beyond economic repair). In mid 1985, the European (NATO) tanker fleets were as follows:

TABLE 5: EUROPEAN TANKER FLEETS (million gross tonnes)	
Denmark	2
France	4
Germany	1
Greece	9
Italy	4
Norway	7
Spain	3
Turkey	1
United Kingdom	6
TOTAL	37

In normal times, there is considerable reliance on the big 'flag of convenience' tanker fleets, but to what extent these would be available in war must be unknown, though experience during the Iran-Iraq war was encouraging.

The decline of the British Merchant Navy is particularly worrying. The number and total size of the British Merchant Navy has been falling faster than most other European countries and is continuing to fall (see Table 7). The House of Commons Defence Committee drew particular attention to the almost total collapse of recruiting of cadets, the seed corn of any future Britain Merchant Navy, and there is no merchant shipbuilding of significance in this country. The failure of successive governments to arrest this decline amounts almost to a wilful weakening of the nation's strategic defences.

Summary

Western Europe needs to import at least 400 million tonnes of oil by sea each year for economic survival and, to a lesser extent, is dependent on a range of other seaborne imports. The Soviet Union has the capability to interrupt this traffic which would lead

TABLE 6: UK MERCHANT FLEET January 1988

	Number	1000 gross tons
Tankers	167	5508
Cross channel ferries	26	182
LNG carriers	19	513
Outsize bulk oil tankers	2	454
Bulk ore carriers	56	1899
Container vessels	46	1311
General cargo, single-deck	185	356
multi-deck	72	604
Passenger vessels	7	378
Ferries	91	159
TOTAL	671	11,025

TABLE 7: THE DECLINE OF BRITISH SHIPPING

Year	Number	Gross tons
1950	3092	17,198
1960	2902	20,202
1970	1977	24,061
1980	1275	25,719
1986	545	11,222

to the rapid collapse of European economies. Defeat at sea for Europe is possible and is probably the most dangerous remaining Soviet threat.

Oil supplies can also be interrupted at source or on route and sea power is essential in any countermeasures.

Appendix 4

Discounting to Net Present Value

Accountants have a neat means of bringing future profits, savings or expenses to an equivalent present value. The calculation is exactly the converse of working out interest on an investment: £100 invested at a rate of 10 percent gives £10 per annum, so the present value of £10 per annum at 10 percent is £100. This calculation is referred to as Discounting to Net Present Value (NPV). Compounding of interest makes the real calculation arithmetically more difficult, but the running costs of a ship (or the savings possible on such costs) can be discounted to a Net Present Value in the same way. For a ship with a life of twenty years, the Net Present Value of the running cost, discounted at 10 percent, works out at about eight times the yearly running cost. For two ships, one of which may be expensive to build but cheap to run and the other cheaper to build but more expensive to run, the running costs can be discounted and added to the building costs as a basis for comparing the total cost of ownership.

The first problem is what discount rate to use, since in practice the rate depends on variables such as the interest rate and the rate of inflation. For government departments the Treasury lays down a figure, usually about 5 percent after removing inflation, but it is said that politicians (who like to play down future expenses) discount at 30 percent, increasing as an election approaches. A second problem is that the running costs of a ship may themselves vary, due to fluctuations in real prices such as that of oil fuel.

Despite these problems, Discounting to Net Present Value does give a useful means of quantifying the through-life running costs of a ship (or indeed the savings possible on such costs) in terms of total present expenditure.

Glossary

AAW	Anti-Aircraft Warfare
ACE	Allied Command Europe
ADV	Air Defence Version (of the Tornado)
AEW	Airborne Early Warning
AIO	Action Information Organisation (US equivalent CIC)
AOR	Ammunition, Oil, and solid stores Replenishment ship
ASS	Aviation Support Ship (cheap helicopter carrier for amphibious operations)
ASVW	Anti-Surface Vessel Weapon
ASW	Anti-Submarine Warfare
COGAG	Combined Gas turbine And Gas turbine (both used at full power)
COGOG	Combined Gas turbine Or Gas turbine (cruising or full power)
CODOG	Combined Diesel Or Gas turbine (diesel cruising, gas full power)
C³I	Command, Control, Communications & Intelligence
DNC	Director of Naval Construction
EH 101	European Helicopter Industries 01 (EH 101 is a misprint which has become common usage). Now named Merlin, said to be another mistyping for Marlin
ESM	Electronic Support Measures
FAAMS	Family of Anti-Aircraft Missiles
HME	Hull Machinery & Electrical; USN for vehicle technology
IMO	International Maritime Organisation
LCAC	Landing Craft Air Cushion

LCL	Landing Craft Logistics
LCU	Landing Craft Utility
LCVP	Landing Craft Vehicle and Personnel
LFE	Lateral Force Estimator
LPD	Landing ship Dock (P seems to be for Personnel)
LSL	Landing Ship Logistics
MAD	Magnetic Anomaly Detection
MCM(V)	Mine Counter Measures (Vessel)
MII	Motion Induced Interruption
NPV	Net Present Value (see Appendix 4)
PAP	Poisson Auto-Propulse (mine disposal fish)
RARDE	Royal Armament Research & Development Establishment
RAM	Radar Absorbing Materials
RAS	Replenishment At Sea
RCNC	Royal Corps of Naval Constructors
RMS	Root Mean Square
ROF	Royal Ordnance Factory
Ro-Ro	Roll on – Roll off
RPV	Remote Piloted Vehicle
SLEP	Ship Life Extension Programme
SOLAS	Safety Of Life At Sea
SOSUS	Sound Systems Under the Sea
SSN	Nuclear attack submarine
SS(B)N	Nuclear-powered Ballistic missile submarine
STUFT	Ships Taken Up From Trade
SWATH	Small Waterplane Area, Twin Hull
T-AGOS	Auxiliary Ocean Surveillance ship (Towed Array)
UPC	Unit Production Cost
VERTREP	Vertical Replenishment (by helicopter)
VLR	Very Long Range
VSTOL	Vertical/Short Take-off and Landing

Index